W9-CHL-757

Tzedakah
A WAY OF LIFE

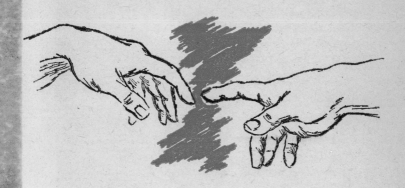

Edited by

AZRIEL EISENBERG

Foreword by PHILIP BERNSTEIN

Illustrated by Janet and Alex D'Amato

BEHRMAN HOUSE, INC. • Publishers • NEW YORK

Library of Congress Catalog Card Number: 63-15993

Manufactured in the United States of America

Table of Contents

continued

Foreword
by Philip Bernstein

IF THERE is one area that identifies and unites Jews, no matter what their personal beliefs and practices, it is *Tzedakah*. *Tzedakah* is more than charity or philanthropy, noble as they are; more than man's humanity to man, exalted as that is; more truly, it is righteousness and justice. Without these qualities civilization would perish.

It is the highest ideal in Jewish teaching—for it is the highest application of Jewish ethical values. It is Judaism in action—and Judaism is inherently and deeply a religion of action, a way of life, a way of living.

What a rich eventful history *Tzedakah* and the Jews, the concept and a people, have woven together! *Tzedakah* is the "golden thread in the design of the great tapestry" which has run through the life of the Jewish people from its very beginnings to this day. The pages of history are adorned with magnificent, glowing tales of this prime force in Jewish life. American Jewry has enriched that heritage—and continues to enrich it—in the story of *Tzedakah* that unfolds in this generation as in perhaps no other.

It is the most distinctive contribution of American Jews to American life; Americans generally have patterned Community Chests and United Funds after the example of Jewish Federations and Welfare Funds, and have emulated standards and methods which Jews have pioneered. Each year the Jews of America mobilize over

5

$200,000,000 for the service and betterment of mankind and society.

We have been fortunate to help produce and share the blessings of America; and we have given constantly changing expression to these timeless ideals to meet new needs, and to seize new opportunities for human advancement. Wherever there is need—in our own neighborhoods and cities, across the nation, or around the world—American Jewish *Tzedakah* is at work. It is finding new cures for old diseases and new ones, it is assuring self-support and self-respect for our aged, it is helping children, strengthening family life, providing vocational retraining, building better understanding and cooperation among different religious and racial groups, bringing people to freedom, and helping in a host of other ways.

And most reassuring is the fact that the younger generation is carrying forward the torch which their mothers and fathers have lovingly handed to them. The idea and the ideal of *Tzedakah* have always been implanted in the earliest years, as the keystone of our lives. In this experience of learning and doing, this little book is a most welcome treasure of lore. Readers will find it a rich resource of tradition and example. Children and their parents will read it with a glow of pleasure, pride and inspiration.

For
JUDAH and MARION

Acknowledgments

I acknowledge my indebtedness to Sam Elkin and Abraham Segal for helping me in editing this book, and to Moses Eskolsky for contributing two stories to it.

AZRIEL EISENBERG

STORIES FROM

THE DAYS OF THE BIBLE

INTRODUCTION—*Share With Others*

FROM OUR very beginning as a people we have been taught to share with the poor, the needy, the handicapped and unfortunate. The Biblical story of Ruth, on which "A Time to Harvest" in this book is based, gives a glimpse of the way our forefathers shared their crops with those in want. Grain left standing in the corners of the field; stray ears dropped during the reaping; sheaves forgotten overnight; fallen grapes, and olives left on the branches after the harvest—all of these ceased to be the property of the owner, but belonged by right to the poor and to the stranger in need. Every third year a farmer was required to put aside a tenth of all his produce to be shared by those in want. And beyond all this, the Children of Israel were taught to be eyes to the blind, feet to the lame, fathers to the fatherless, and brothers to whoever was an alien in their midst.

"The rich and the poor meet together: the Lord is the maker of them all." So runs a proverb well known in Biblical times. And from the beginning *Tzedakah,* the care of the well-to-do for the poor, was not merely voluntary or optional. Rather, it was governed by exact rules. Thus, poor people were to be allowed to glean in the fields not once but three times every day. For some, said our wise men, would have infants at home, and would need food early in the morning; but there might be others who could not come out to the fields until midday, and still others—especially the older folk—who could not come out until evening. Relatives had to be

considered first. A Jew had to help his neighbors before he helped strangers, the poor of his own family before the poor of the city, and the poor of his own city before the poor of another city.

If a man and a woman both needed help, the woman had to be attended to first, and then the man after her. "A woman is more modest than a man, and her feelings are more easily hurt. Therefore, a poor woman should always be clothed and fed before a man, and not after."

If a poor man requested clothing, he might be questioned and challenged and asked to prove that he needed it. But if a man asked for food, it must be given to him immediately, without question. The hungry must not be kept waiting . . .

A farmer could not show favor to certain needy people because he liked them better than others, if that meant keeping anything from those he didn't like. "Anyone who refuses one person and gives to another," said the law, "is a robber of the poor."

The stories that follow deal with *Tzedakah* in Biblical times. They are culled from the Midrash and from Jewish folklore.

Abraham Learns a Lesson

Because God was kind to him, Abraham was a great and wealthy man, with a large family, many servants, huge herds of cattle, and tents, and possessions without number.

To show his gratitude to God for his good fortune, Abraham set up at a crossroad the largest and most brightly colored tent. He left the tent open at all four sides, so that any traveler, whether he came from north, south, east, or west, could enter the tent, find food and drink, water for washing, a bed for sleeping, and someone to wait upon him.

Many weary wanderers came to the tent, washed away their weariness, fed their bodies, and relaxed in sleep. When they were ready to depart, with a sack of food for their journey, they would often ask for Abraham, to thank him for his kindness. But Abraham, smiling away their thanks, would only teach them to believe in One God, and to worship Him.

Thus, Abraham carried out God's commandment to do *Tzedakah*.

But one day a weak old man entered Abraham's tent and rested there. When, recovering his strength, the old man tried to thank him, Abraham said: "Don't thank me, my friend. Whatever I have given you was first given to me. The God of all men shares His good world with us all. Thank *Him!*"

The old man frowned. "Why should I give thanks to *your* God?" he said. "I have my own god right here

in my sack. *He* is the one who led me to your tent, and *he* is the one I intend to thank."

The old man took out a small, ugly wooden statue, kissed it, bowed to it, praised its power and its glory, and promised to honor it as long as he lived.

A fury gripped Abraham: "How dare you worship an idol at the very door of my tent, and after I have shown you kindness as commanded by God?"

Abraham seized the old man's idol, smashed it to the ground, grasped the old man by the neck, and thrust him bodily out of the tent.

"Go, old fool!" he cried. "My hospitality was wasted on you! Get out and never come back here again!"

The old man limped away without a word. Abraham, still red in the face and breathing heavily, opened his mouth to call for a servant to sweep up the pieces of the broken idol; but at the first syllable he suddenly choked off his call. Clearly and distinctly he heard a Voice in his ear, a Voice he had heard many times before, a small, soft voice that seemed to be far away and yet was right inside of him at the same time; it was a Heavenly Voice.

"Abraham!" the Voice called.

Instantly, Abraham answered: "Yes, Lord?"

The Voice continued: "The man you chased away is eighty years old. For all those years I protected him and cared for him. Though he worshiped idols made by his own hands, I did not hate him. He, too, is My son, My child—even as you are! You, Abraham, fed him and helped him only once, only for a little time. Yet, because he would not obey you, you mistreated him. Was this well done—to take upon yourself to decide who deserves *Tzedakah* and who does not?"

The Voice paused, and Abraham felt a sharp remorse. He bowed his head, and hid his eyes, and wept.

"Now go, Abraham!" whispered the near-far Voice. "Go find the old man. Humble yourself before him and bring him back. Make him welcome. Serve him. He is old and weak. He has loved his idols from childhood. He knows no better. But you, Abraham, you *do* know better. You know the one true God. You know the meaning of *Tzedakah*. Go!"

As always, Abraham obeyed the Voice of God.

Adapted from a story by Benjamin Franklin

The Stray Lamb

WHEN Moses fled from Egypt's Pharaoh he went to live with his father-in-law, Jethro, in the land of Midian. There, Moses spent his days living the life of a simple shepherd. He pastured Jethro's flocks on the desert shrubs, he wandered with the sheep as they hunted for the best places to graze. He looked after the needs of his flock. Tenderly, he cared for them when they were hurt. He knew each sheep and each lamb. And Jethro was happy to entrust his sheep to the faithful and loving hands of Moses.

Indeed, it seemed that Moses had resigned himself to spending the rest of his life as a shepherd.

But even then, Moses could not push out of his mind the thought that his people were still slaves in the land of Pharaoh. Often he dreamed of the day when God would free the Children of Israel, and lead them into their own country—the Land of Israel.

One day Moses led his flock across the desert to the foot of Mount Sinai, a great mountain with many craggy rocks and a towering peak. In the mountain's shadow, the flock grazed peacefully, nibbling at the sparse grass. At sunset Moses prepared to lead his flock home. But when he counted them, he noticed that a young lamb, only three days old, was missing. Looking around, he quickly saw that the lamb's tiny hoofprints led toward the mountain.

A sandstorm was brewing. Soon clouds of sand would rise, the cold desert night would set in; and so

Moses pondered: Should he lead his flock to Jethro's home, leaving the stray lamb to its fate? Or should he leave the flock and climb the mountain in search of the lamb?

The thought of the tender little lamb alone on the mountain in the coming windstorm, the thought of the dangerous crags, the thought of its weakness and helplessness, were too much for Moses. He began to climb the mountain. He knew that if he did not return with the flock by sunset, Jethro would send other shepherds to bring the sheep home.

The sandstorm broke as Moses started up the cliffs of Sinai. Higher and higher he climbed. Cold wind penetrated his cloak. Sand drove against every pore of his skin. A driving rain began to fall. Rocks grew slippery, hardly providing a foothold. And still Moses searched behind every bush, beneath every ledge. All night long he searched, while the storm grew fiercer and fiercer.

Toward morning he found the lamb. It was weak from hunger and cold. Crouching against a rock, unable to stand on its own legs, it was more dead than alive. A little longer and it would have perished.

Quickly Moses lifted the lamb and held it under his robe, against his chest, giving it the warmth from his own body. And quickly, too, he ran down the steep mountainside, heedless of his own safety.

It was almost dawn when he arrived at the foot of the mountain. He was about to run across the valley to Jethro's home when he noticed a mysterious glow in the darkness. A bush was wrapped in flames, even though it was drenched by the rain. As Moses watched, the flames grew brighter and brighter, yet the bush did not burn

up. Marveling at the sight, he stood motionless in fear and wonder.

Suddenly there came a Voice that seemed to rise from the very heart of the burning bush: "Moses! You have risked your own life to rescue a stray lamb. God has chosen you to save *His* flock, the Children of Israel, from slavery in Egypt. You shall lead them to a land flowing with milk and honey. God will be with you and this shall be your sign: When you bring out the Children of Israel, you will worship God on this very mountain!"

Moses stumbled away from the burning bush, filled with awe. He was still clutching the lamb to his breast; and it was then that he realized that just as he was carrying the lamb in his arms, he had been chosen to carry the future of his people in his heart and mind.

From the Midrash

A Time to Harvest

GOLDEN stalks of wheat and barley fell before the flashing scythes of the reapers. Following them, the binders bent and tied the sheaves into bundles. And following the binders, the gatherers lifted and carried the sheaves to the threshing-floor. The fields of Bethlehem hummed with work and song and jest.

It was harvest time in ancient Israel.

Since dawn, the farmer Boaz, his wife Ruth, and their sons had worked in the fields along with their men. It was nearly noon when Boaz, straightening his back, saw a wanderer on the road. A mangy little donkey followed him. Both man and beast looked tired and hungry.

"The Lord be with you, stranger!" called Boaz. "Come here and pluck some of our grain!"

The wanderer approached cautiously. With a wary eye on Boaz, he plucked some grain and tasted it. The donkey brayed, but the man pushed it away with his other hand.

Boaz said: "Take some from the corner too, friend."

The stranger looked puzzled.

"When we reap our grain," Boaz explained, "we always leave the corner of the field standing. The corner is for travelers and poor people."

The wanderer said nothing. He plucked more grain from the corner of Boaz's field. He beat it out, rubbed it, and placed the kernels in his pouch. The donkey brayed again, and the stranger yanked on his pull-rope and turned back to the road.

"This farmer is crazy," he muttered to himself.

Boaz's voice stopped him. "Why do you shame me, stranger? I've done you no wrong."

The wanderer turned, startled. "Shame you?" he said. "I'm a stranger. I've just come from the land of Moab. I've never even seen your face until today. Why should I want to shame you?"

"But you stand in my field," Boaz said sorrowfully. "You see my men binding the sheaves and you don't stop to gather the gleanings."

"Gleanings?" repeated the puzzled stranger. He wiped the sweat off his face and shoved his donkey away from his pouch.

Boaz nodded. "The reaper grasps a handful of stalks and his scythe cuts them off from below. Stalks that slip from the hand and escape the scythe—they're not for the reaper. The Lord commands them to be left for the poor and the stranger."

"The Lord?" said the wanderer, a glimmer of understanding crossing his face. "You mean the Lord who owns this field?"

Boaz smiled. "Yes. Now please gather up some of our gleanings."

The stranger shrugged, took up some fallen stalks, and rubbed them in his hands to free the kernels. Keeping the donkey off with his elbow, he thrust the kernels into his pouch. Then he bowed politely to Boaz.

"The Lord who owns this field," he said, "is most generous." He looked about him. "I suppose he's over yonder at the threshing-floor."

"The Lord who owns this field," Boaz replied, "is there—here—everywhere."

"I'll move on then, friend." The wanderer yanked again on his rope, but again Boaz's voice stopped him.

"The forgotten! Don't you see the men gathering sheaves to the threshing-floor? Are you going away without collecting the forgotten?"

The wanderer looked over Boaz, long and carefully. "Forgive me. But I'm afraid I don't know what this forgotten is."

"Why, when a man gathers sheaves and forgets any sheaves behind him, those sheaves are reserved only for wanderers and the needy. Any left-over sheaves you see on the ground, the Lord has told us to let them stay. They belong to you."

Silently the wanderer went and found the forgotten sheaves, beat them out, rubbed them, and placed the kernels in his pouch. Then he untied the pouch from around his waist and placed it atop the donkey's back.

"Getting heavy," he said, grinning at Boaz. "I am very grateful. There's enough in my pouch to last me several days." To the donkey he snapped, "Move on, there!"

"I'll walk a little way with you," Boaz said. "I don't want you to miss some fine grape and olive orchards farther up the road."

The two men walked side by side, the wanderer looking a bit dazed. The donkey trudged after them with head drooping low.

"Tell me, friend," said the wanderer, "does the same Lord own the orchards, too?"

"Of course! He owns *every* field."

The stranger eyed Boaz and thought: He *is* crazy. He glanced back at the pouch on the donkey's back and

thought: That goes for his Lord, too. But may everyone
I meet be just as crazy.

Aloud, the stranger said, "I wonder, is there any
danger of shaming a grape and olive grower?"

"Just hurry past an orchard without taking the topmost and you will find out," Boaz said with a smile.

"Topmost," the stranger repeated. "Topmost grapes
on a vine? Topmost olives on a branch?"

"Right. They belong to you. Also, any imperfect
grapes or olives on each branch." Boaz stopped to pick
up a basket. "Eat what you like, and take the rest along
with you in this basket."

The wanderer tied his donkey to a thorn-bush, and
began to pluck and eat the juicy grapes. "Delicious," he
mumbled from a full mouth. He tried the olives, too,
and filled the basket to the brim. The donkey tried to
nibble at some thorns, but finally gave up. Boaz silently
watched both the man and the donkey.

"This has certainly been a day full of surprises for
me," remarked the stranger. "I was hungry and tired
when I came here. You welcomed me, fed me, and provided for my long road ahead."

"Not I," said Boaz.

"I know, I know," said the wanderer. "The Lord
who owns these fields and orchards. Well, I'd like to
thank him. What's his name and where will I find him?"

"I've already told you where to find Him. He is
everywhere. But you can find Him only in your heart
and the hearts of your fellow men. He is the Lord God
of Israel. He owns the earth and everything in it. His
Torah teaches us to share our land joyfully with the
poor and the needy."

The stranger stared at Boaz. "And how," he demanded, "do I thank this Lord God of yours?"

Boaz pointed to the stranger's donkey. "By treating your animal—and everyone—and everything—as I have treated you. As the Lord God of Israel treats us all. By freely and gladly sharing what you have with others."

The wanderer looked at his drooping donkey. Then he looked at Boaz, and the orchard, and the hot blue sky overhead. Then he looked at his donkey again, and went over to it and began to untie the pouch of grain.

Adapted from a story by Yehudah Steinberg

Brotherly Love

LONG AGO, on the site of old Jerusalem, the holy city, lived two brothers. They were farmers, and tilled the land they had inherited from their father. The older one was unmarried, living alone. The younger was married and lived with his wife and four children. The brothers loved each other dearly and did not want to divide the fields between them. Together they plowed, planted, and harvested the same crop. After they cut the wheat, they shared equally in the produce of the earth.

One night during the harvest, the older brother lay down to sleep. But his thoughts were troubled. "Here I am," he told himself, "all alone, with no wife and no children. I don't need to feed or clothe anyone. But my brother has the responsibility of a family. Is it right to share our harvest equally? After all, he needs more than I do!"

At midnight he arose and took a pile of sheaves from his crop, carried them to his brother's field, and left them there. Then he returned to his tent and went to sleep in peace.

That same night, his brother also could not sleep. He thought about his older brother. "Here I am," he said. "When I grow old, my children will take care of me. But what will happen to my brother, in *his* old age? Who will take care of *his* needs? It isn't fair to divide the crops equally!"

So he arose and took a load of sheaves and brought

them to his brother's field and left them there. Then he
returned home and went to sleep in peace.

When morning came, both brothers were amazed
to find their crops exactly as they had been the night
before. They wondered greatly, but did not speak to
each other about this strange event.

The next night each brother repeated his action.

When morning came, again they were amazed to find they had the same number of sheaves as the night before.

But on the third night, when each of the brothers was carrying a pile of sheaves to the other, they met at the top of the hill. Suddenly they understood. They dropped their sheaves; they embraced, weeping with gratitude and happiness, and returned to their tents.

The Lord saw this act of love between brothers and blessed the place where they met that night. And when, in the course of time, King Solomon built the Temple, from which peace and love were to flow to the whole world, it was erected on that very spot.

From Jewish Folklore

The Flour Barrel and the Water Jar

FAMINE had come to the land of Israel. No rain fell. The brooks and the wells dried up. The grain and vegetables failed to grow. Throughout the land people suffered hunger and thirst.

The prophet Elijah suffered along with the people. He pitied them. He prayed to God to send them rain.

One hot day Elijah set out to walk among the people. Soon he became hungry and thirsty. Passing along a dusty road, he saw a little cottage where a widow lived with her small son.

Elijah asked the widow for a drink of water. At a glance, the widow saw that the dusty stranger was hot and tired and thirsty. All the water she had was in a little jar she had managed to save through the dry spell. This she had been carefully rationing out to her small son and to herself. Nevertheless, without hesitation, she poured the stranger a cool and refreshing drink.

Elijah's spirits revived. "Thank you," he said. "Can you also, perhaps, spare a bite of bread? I haven't eaten all day."

"I would gladly," said the widow, "but I haven't a crumb in the house. I have just a handful of flour and a few drops of oil. I was about to bake a small loaf for my boy and myself. You are more than welcome to share it with us."

The widow built up a small fire, scraped the flour barrel for the last few grains, emptied the oil jar of its few drops, and baked the smallest loaf of bread Elijah had ever seen. Even a small boy could eat the loaf by himself and still remain hungry.

Inviting Elijah to sit at the table with them, the widow divided the tiny loaf into three parts. She gave the largest piece to her guest, and the next largest to her son; the smallest she kept for herself. Then, thanking God for the bread, they began their meager meal.

Having drunk, eaten, and rested Elijah thanked the widow again and continued his journey among the people. But before he left he said: "You gave me water

when I was thirsty, and fed me when I was hungry. You did this although you didn't have enough for your son and yourself. God will help you. Neither you nor your son will lack food and water, no matter how long the famine lasts."

The widow thanked Elijah. She did not take his words seriously. To her, he was just a grateful stranger.

But the next day, when the pangs of hunger seized her son and herself, she looked longingly at the empty flour barrel and water jar, and saw a miraculous sight. The barrel she had emptied only the day before now held exactly the same amount of flour as she had used up for the meal with the stranger. The water jar held exactly the same amount of water as the stranger had drunk.

Joyfully, the widow baked a small loaf for herself and her son. And from that day on, until the rains came and food was plentiful again, the widow's flour barrel always contained enough flour for a loaf of bread as large as the one she had shared with the prophet Elijah.

Jewish Folk Tale

STORIES FROM

THE DAYS OF THE TALMUD

INTRODUCTION—*Learn How to Give*

WHEN THE Romans conquered Palestine, destroyed the holy Temple and exiled the Jewish people, the heritage of the Bible went with them. Its teachings, especially the ideals of *Tzedakah* and social justice, were their constitution. Such became the reputation of the Jews that the Roman emperor Justinian (483-565) observed that there were no beggars found among them in his time. Indeed, with some Jews *Tzedakah* became such a passion that to curb their zeal the Rabbis found it necessary to make a rule that no one was to give away more than one-fifth of his income. But on the other hand they continued to teach that no city was worth living in, which had no organization for giving relief.

To keep their people continually reminded of their duty, the Rabbis prescribed this exhortation, to be said at the morning service on every day of the week: "These are the things whose value a man enjoys while he lives, and from which he also benefits in the world to come: honoring father and mother, the practice of kindness, hospitality to strangers, visiting the sick, outfitting the bride, attending the dead to the grave, devotion in prayer, and making peace between fellow men . . ."

And on Sabbath morning, while the Scroll of the Torah was still on the reader's table, the worshipers were to give thanks to all who occupied themselves faithfully in the work of *Tzedakah*: "May the Holy One, blessed be He, reward them, keep them well and strong and happy! May He forgive their sins, and send them blessing and success in everything they do!" So important is this prayer that our *Siddur* (Prayer Book) includes it twice in the service—once in Hebrew and again in Aramaic, the everyday language of the Jews for many centuries.

The Jews were cautioned by the Rabbis, never to shame the poor, even by the most insignificant act. "Better to give no charity at all," our holy books warn us, "than to give to the poor in public." In the ancient Temple, and in many a synagogue afterward, a special room stayed open twenty-four hours a day. Anyone could enter, but only one person might do so at a time. Thus nobody could know for what reason any man entered the room except the man himself. He might be a rich man leaving an offering; he might be a poor man in need of money to feed his family; he might even be a thief—but nobody could know.

"Happy is he who considers the poor wisely," said the Psalmist. In giving charity one may do harm to the needy—harm that may even outweigh the good. One rabbi, on seeing a man handing a gift to a poor fellow in a public place, rebuked him by saying, "You would have been more charitable had you saved his honor and not offered him the gift."

Acts of giving charity, in addition to their social value, were considered *Mitzvot*, religious deeds. Even the poor, those who themselves receive charity, have to contribute their mite to the Charity Fund. Thus the very idea of *Tzedakah* was, from early times, a great all-inclusive democratic institution in Jewish life and tradition.

The teachings of the Rabbis are reflected in the stories from the Talmud and the Midrash that follow. And they are summed up by the most celebrated of all rabbinic scholars, Maimonides, on pages 47 and 48.

"TEMPLE ISRAEL"

When the Temple Was Gone

DURING a war in the time of the Roman Empire, Rabbi Yohanan ben Zakkai had escaped from Jerusalem in a funeral casket. Now the war was over and he was returning. It was early spring, and the weather was raw and cold. The countryside was destroyed. It looked bleak and bare. Everything was in ruins.

Rabbi Yohanan was followed by his friend and pupil, Rabbi Joshua. Both men walked along with heads bowed and shoulders sagging. The winds swirled about them as they gazed in stunned silence at the desolation.

Once, the Temple Mount and its court had been a golden place. Now weeds and thorns grew among the fallen stones and pillars.

Rabbi Joshua could stand the sight no longer. He burst out: "All gone, the splendor of Israel! Jerusalem ruined! Our Temple destroyed! No longer do we have a house of God! No longer can we worship Him! The world itself has come to an end!"

It was then that Rabbi Yohanan's quiet but firm voice was raised: "Enough, my son. Look, but do not weep! Did not our teachers say that the world rests upon three things?"

"Yes, Rabbi," answered Rabbi Joshua. "Upon study of Torah, upon worship in the Temple, and upon doing of kind deeds."

Rabbi Yohanan put his arm around his friend's shoulders. "And have we not been taught that mercy and the knowledge of God are greater than the sacrifices of the Temple?"

"The prophet Hosea said it," said Rabbi Joshua.

"Then be of good cheer, Joshua, my son. The synagogue will be our House of God. Israel will study and worship and practice *Tzedakah* in the synagogue. Israel will live, and not die. The world will stand, and not fall."

So saying, Rabbi Yohanan walked ahead, and Rabbi Joshua followed, his head raised once more, and his eyes envisioned the clearing away of the rubble of war.

From Aboth de Rabbi Nathan

The Gift of Greatness

A CERTAIN Abba Judah lived in Antioch. He always contributed generously to funds for needy scholars. But it happened one day that when three rabbis, Eliezer, Joshua, and Akiba, came to his home to receive a contribution, Abba Judah was in a difficult situation. He had lost most of his wealth. Ashamed at not being able to give as in the past, he said to his wife, "The rabbis have come for contributions, and I don't know what to do."

His wife, who was even more pious than her husband, replied, "You still have one field left. Sell half of it, and give the money to the rabbis."

Abba Judah did just that. When the rabbis learned of his unselfish generosity, they blessed him and said, "May your needs be supplied."

Shortly afterward, Abba Judah began to plow the half of the field which was still his. His cow stumbled and split her hoof. When Abba Judah stooped to help her, he saw a rich treasure lying in the ground. Instantly he said: "Surely, it was for my sake that God made the cow stumble and split her hoof."

When the rabbis again visited Antioch, they asked how Abba Judah was getting along.

"I'm as wealthy as ever," replied Abba Judah. "I own many camels, sheep, and cows. It was your prayer that brought me this good result."

"Your own acts brought you good results," the rabbis replied. "Others gave more than you when we were

last in this city, but we placed your name at the head
of our list."

The rabbis sat down to dinner with Abba Judah and
said in his honor the verse in Proverbs 18:16: "A man's
gift makes room for him, and brings him before great
men."

From the Jerusalem Talmud

The Survivor

STROLLING along the shore one day, Rabbi Elazar ben Shammua saw a ship sinking in the sea. Only one survivor, clinging to a spar and buffeted by the waves, finally reached the coast. He was completely naked.

Some Jews were passing by on their way to a festival at Jerusalem, and the survivor said to them: "I am of the children of Esau, your brother. Please give me a garment to cover myself. The sea has stripped me of all I own."

But they replied: "May your people also be stripped."

The survivor caught sight of Rabbi Elazar. "I see you are an old and honorable man," he said. "You deserve everyone's respect. Deal kindly with me. Give me a garment, so that I may cover myself."

Rabbi Elazar gave him a robe, and taking him home, he fed and clothed the poor man. Then the Rabbi gave the survivor two hundred dinars and sent him on his way.

Soon afterward the wicked emperor who ruled in the land of Israel died. A new emperor came to the throne—and of all people, he was the survivor who had been helped by Rabbi Elazar!

One of the first acts of the new emperor was to pass a law that all Jewish men should be killed and all Jewish women be taken in captivity.

Terror sped into the hearts of all Jews in the land of Israel. Jewish elders ran to Rabbi Elazar and begged him to go to plead for them with the new emperor.

The Rabbi said: "Don't you know that for nothing the government does nothing?"

And so the Jewish elders gave Rabbi Elazar four thousand dinars.

Rabbi Elazar went to the palace gate, where he said to the guards, "Tell the Emperor there is a Jew at the gate who wishes to see his Majesty."

Unaware of his visitor's identity, the Emperor granted permission for the Jew to enter the palace. Rabbi Elazar was escorted to the throne room. And immediately, when the Emperor saw who was approaching the throne, he threw himself to the ground and bowed down before Rabbi Elazar.

"What is my lord's business?" cried the Emperor. "And why has he troubled to come here?"

"I have come to plead for the Jews," Rabbi Elazar replied in astonishment at recognizing the man he had befriended. "I beg you to be merciful and abolish the law against them."

The Emperor arose and asked, "Does your Torah contain anything in it that is false?"

"No."

"But is it not written in your Torah: 'The Ammonite and the Moabite shall not enter the congregation of the Lord'—because they refused you bread and water in your wanderings on the desert? And am I not a son of Esau, your brother? Yet the Jews showed me no loving-kindness when I was suffering. And he who transgresses the Torah is to be punished by death."

Rabbi Elazar conceded the guilt of the Jews. "But," he said, "forgive them and have mercy."

"Don't you know that for nothing the government does nothing?"

"I have four thousand dinars. Please accept them and have mercy."

The Emperor considered; then he spoke: "The four thousand are yours in exchange for the two hundred you gave me in my time of need. The Jews shall be spared for your sake in exchange for the food and clothing you gave me when I needed them. Now go to my treasury and choose seven robes, in exchange for the one robe you gave me when I was naked. Go back in peace to your people, who are forgiven for your sake."

To Rabbi Elazar may be applied the verse: "Cast thy bread upon the waters."

From the Midrash

Alexander of Macedon

Once upon a time in ancient Greece there was a mighty ruler named Alexander of Macedon. He was a great general, a conqueror of many lands, and he was continually seeking new conquests.

It happened one day that Alexander came to the country of Cassia. The king of Cassia showed Alexander his treasures, but Alexander was impatient with him.

"I did not come here to see your gold. I want to see your customs," he said.

As he spoke, two men came before the king with a case for judgment. "O King," one began, "I bought a ruined piece of land from this stubborn fellow. And when I began to clear the rubbish, I found in the ground a huge chest of gold and precious stones. I asked him to take the fortune, for it belongs to him. I bought only the land, not the treasure."

The former owner of the land disagreed. "I don't *want* this treasure. It doesn't really belong to me. I sold the ruin and everything in it."

The king turned to the first complainant and said: "Have you a son?"

"Yes," was the reply.

The king turned to the second man. "Have you a daughter?" he asked.

"Yes," was the reply again.

"Then," said the king, "let the two young people be married and enjoy the treasure together."

Hearing this judgment, Alexander was quite aston-

ished, both by the peculiarity of the complaint and by the judgment of the king.

"Why are you so puzzled?" asked the king. "Haven't I judged the case properly?"

"Certainly not!"

"What would you have done in your country?"

Said Alexander: "I would have had both men beheaded, and then the treasure would have belonged to me."

The king thought about that remark for a moment. Then he said, "Tell me, Alexander, does the sun shine in your country?"

"Of course."

"Does it rain in your country?"

"Certainly."

"Then you have cattle in your country?"

"Naturally," said Alexander, looking at the king with annoyance.

"Aha!" exclaimed the king. "It is only because of the cattle that the sun shines and the rain falls in your country."

"What are you talking about?" Alexander asked.

The king smiled. "According to your logic," he said, "human beings do not deserve the gifts of sun and rain that come from God."

From the Midrash

Abba Tahnah and the Sick Man

THE sun was sinking toward the west. It was late Friday afternoon, and soon the Sabbath would begin. Abba Tahnah was making his way home to his village. He had been away from home for almost a week. Despite the heavy bundle he carried, he walked rapidly. He was eager to join his wife and children, and he wanted to reach home before the Sabbath.

Suddenly he heard a man's voice calling to him weakly, "Rabbi, Rabbi, please help me. I am sick and lame and cannot walk. Please carry me to the village."

Abba Tahnah stopped short. Instinctively, he wanted to respond to the call for help. But conflicting thoughts raced through his mind.

If I act charitably toward this man, he thought, I will be obeying the word of God. But then I will have to leave my bundle here. I cannot carry both. And if I leave my bundle, how will I feed my wife and children? Caring for one's family is also the command of God. Which shall I carry to the village—this man, or my family's food?

Tahnah's indecision lasted for just a moment. In the very next moment he felt slightly ashamed of himself for the doubt that had crossed his mind about what he should properly do. He set his bundle down, stooped over the sick man, lifted him carefully to his shoulders, and said, "Don't worry. I'll take you to the village."

Though he was already tired, and though the sick man weighed much more than his bundle, Tahnah set

out briskly for the village. Arriving there, he took the
man to his home, saw to his needs, and then turned back
along the road to pick up his bundle.

But the sun was now sinking in the west. Never in
his life had Abba Tahnah broken the Sabbath. But neither had he ever neglected his family on the Sabbath.
Would he be able to bring the bundle home before the
sun finally set? Already it was low in the western sky,
tinging the horizon with gold.

Tahnah ran to where he had left his bundle. He
swung it to his shoulder and started out on his second
journey to the village with a prayer in his heart that God

help him reach home before the Sabbath is ushered in.

But as he passed through the gates, dusk fell. Head bowed and face flushed with shame, Tahnah hurried through the streets. His heart grew heavy as he passed people on their way to the synagogue, and heard them whispering among themselves: "Can this be Abba Tahnah the Pious? Here it is practically the Sabbath already, and he is walking around with a bundle on his shoulders. A Sabbath-breaker!"

Bitterly, the rabbi rebuked himself. "If I have broken the Sabbath, God forgive me!"

Suddenly, bright sunshine flooded the sky. The whole world was lit up as though it had been noon. And a Heavenly Voice came forth:

"Abba Tahnah, the Pious! You have put a stranger's needs before your own. Go home, my son. Eat your bread and drink your wine with a merry heart, for your reward is great. The Sabbath will wait for you!"

From the Midrash

The Ladder of Tzedakah

THE Jewish ideals of *Tzedakah* were taught by Maimonides, our greatest rabbi and leader of eight hundred years ago. *Tzedakah,* said Maimonides, is like a ladder: it has eight steps, from low to high, from worst to best.

Here we give Maimonides' "Eight Degrees of Tzedakah." Every Jew should decide which step of the ladder *he* stands on, and how he can best move upward another step.

1. The lowest step in giving *Tzedakah* is to give too little, and as if "forced" to give.
2. The next step is, though giving too little, to do so pleasantly and cheerfully, as if happy to give.
3. The third step is to give as much as is needed, but only after being asked for it.
4. The fourth step is to give as much as is needed and to do so *before* being asked for it.
5. A fifth and higher step than all these is to give enough and to give before being asked, and to give in such a way that the poor person knows who gives him help, but the helper does not know who the poor person is. (For instance, some of our sages would tie money in the corner of a cloth and toss it over their shoulder as they walked, so that a poor man behind them could pick it up without being recognized.)
6. Sixth on the "Ladder of *Tzedakah*" is to give enough and before being asked, but in such a

47

way that the giver knows who gets the charity, but the receiver doesn't know who has given it to him. (For instance, many great sages used to toss money into the doorway of a poor family as they passed along the street.)

7. The seventh and the next to the highest way to give *Tzedakah* is to do it so that neither the giver nor the receiver knows the other. (For instance, through the secret *Tzedakah* room in the Temple and in the synagogues, or by leaving money on tombstones of famous men, or by giving to a general welfare fund that is managed by trustworthy and efficient trustees.)

8. Finally, at the very top of the "*Tzedakah* Ladder," is the step of helping a needy person by lending him money to open a business, or joining him in a partnership, or finding him a job, so that he can support himself and not *need* charity.

Adapted from Maimonides' Mishneh Torah

(Our Jewish Federation and Welfare Funds today, by and large, do carry out steps seven and eight. When we give to Federation, we never know just who receives our help, and the needy person never knows just who gave it. The very person giving to the Community Fund benefits *from* it too. And Federation always tries not only to help ease the immediate trouble a person is in, but to help him become strong, healthy, self-supporting —so that he needs no more help!)

STORIES FROM

THE MIDDLE AGES

Be Responsible for Your Brother

WHEN THE Jews became dispersed throughout the world, their manner of living was altered. They no longer had a political state. Their ways of life changed completely. *Tzedakah,* although no longer the law of the land, nevertheless served its purpose as the law of God. The synagogue became the center for the care of the poor, the needy, the wronged and the stranger, as well as for prayer and study.

Living scattered in foreign cities where they earned their livelihood as merchants and artisans, the Jews found life more complicated. *Tzedakah* had to be organized. A poor man could no longer simply come and take food from a farmer's field or orchard. Money had to be collected, and kept available for those in need.

It was thus that *Tzedakah* funds came to be organized. There was a general fund, called the *Kuppah* or Chest—just as in American cities today there is often a general fund known as the Community Chest. To the *Kuppah* each Jew had to contribute according to his means; generally he gave a tithe or tenth of his income. A man was expected to give voluntarily, but if necessary the rabbis and the community could force a man to contribute. A man called up to the reading of the Torah usually donated to the *Kuppah* for the honor. At weddings, births, Bar Mitzvahs, and *Yahrzeits* (memorials for the dead), people also made contributions. And of course in emergencies, when misfortune struck the community and more was needed than was in the *Kuppah*, special appeals were made in every synagogue, so that those in want could be taken care of.

Every synagogue had its *Gabbaim* or trustees, chosen from among the most honored and respected Jews of the city, who worked for the Jewish community without pay. Every day the *Gabbaim* collected funds for the *Kuppah*, and regularly on *Erev Shabbat* (Fridays) they distributed these funds to the poor to help them through the coming week.

In order to avoid the least suspicion of dishonesty the *Gabbaim* always collected funds by a committee of two or more. In deciding to give out the funds, there were three members. This was to avoid a deadlock in any argument over how to distribute the money, since there would always be a vote of two to one in any dispute. The Jews did not leave *Tzedakah* to chance!

In emergencies the *Gabbaim* gathered and distributed food, clothing, and medicines. They were in charge of orphans, the outfitting of poor brides, the burial of those who died penniless, the education of poor children, the lending of money to businessmen in need, and many other forms of relief and social work.

In many places the activities of *Tzedakah* centered in the synagogue courtyard. Here stood the inn or *Hakhnasat Orhim* ("welcoming the wayfarer"), the *Hekdesh* (community hospital), and the Talmud Torah, the Hebrew Free School—institutions which were the forerunners of today's large philanthropic centers. Here, too, wedding ceremonies took place in the open, often on a Friday afternoon, so that the celebrants could usher in the Sabbath and at the same time provide a gala Sabbath meal for the needy.

The traveling merchant or student, the wandering collector for charity, the refugee or the dispossessed person, always came to the synagogue. He could always count, at the end of the Friday evening service, on being invited to someone's home as a "Sabbath guest." Here he would enjoy a home-cooked meal, company, a bed, and often a gift "for the road."

Our synagogue customs today still remind us that the House of God was once actually a lodging place for the homeless. For example, why is the *Kiddush* said in synagogue on Friday evenings, at the close of the service? The answer is given by our wise men: "We chant *Kiddush* in the synagogue in order to give the wayfarers who eat, drink, and sleep there an opportunity to hear the blessing over the wine." For the same reason a *Sukkah* was always built near the synagogue during the festival of Sukkot, even though every Jewish household had one of its own.

In each community, dozens of societies performed various works of *Gemilut Hasadim* (loving-kindness). In Rome, for example, Jews established societies in charge of visiting the sick and of arranging burials. There were seven different organizations for providing clothes and bedding for children, widows, and prisoners. Two societies supplied poor brides with gifts, clothes, and wedding expenses. Another helped people going to settle in the Holy Land. Still others supported Hebrew schools, inns for travelers, arranged for religious services in the homes of mourners, and provided for the Sabbath and holiday needs of the poor and the stranger.

Each society had its own picturesque name, taken from the Bible or the *Siddur* (Prayer Book): Clothers of the Naked, Lighters of Sabbath Candles, Sponsors of Brides, Upbringers of Orphans, Crown of the Aged (for old people), Tree of Life (a society for education), Comforters of Mourners . . .

Today, in our Jewish community life, we see almost exactly the same thing. Present-day Federations are like the community chest, the *Kuppah* of long ago. Burial societies still exist in many American cities. The Passover Matzot Fund, the modern orphanage, our free Jewish schools, and many other institutions have come down to us from our fathers of long ago.

The stories that follow come mainly from Jewish folklore of medieval days.

The Sabbath Mission

Long ago there lived a pious, God-fearing merchant, named Mordecai.

On Friday mornings, Mordecai would entrust his vast business affairs to his assistants, and would set out to visit all the Jews in the community. It was a ritual with him to ask for money and food, which could be given to the needy for the Sabbath. At the end of the day he divided all the gifts into three parts—one for widows, one for orphans, and one for poor students.

But in the course of time Mordecai's business failed and he became one of the poorest men in town. To make a living, he entered into partnership with a friend, and they opened a small shop. But on Fridays he continued his life-long custom, taking up his charity-sack and making his rounds, collecting for the poor.

However, when Mordecai reached a ripe old age, it began to be difficult for him to make his rounds. One day, as he was carrying his half-filled charity-sack, Mordecai paused to lean heavily on his cane. He was tired. The prophet Elijah, seeing his trouble, appeared before him in the disguise of a stranger.

"Friend," said Elijah, "that bag is heavy, and you are not young any longer. Let me carry it for you."

"No, thank you," replied Mordecai. "All my life I have performed this *Mitzvah,* and I don't intend to give it up now."

Finally, Elijah persuaded Mordecai to accept his help for a short while. As soon as he rounded a corner,

Elijah stopped and filled the bag almost to the top with gold coins. These he covered with a thin layer of fish, *halleh,* cake, and other Sabbath foods. Returning to Mordecai, he said: "Here, I've collected a few gifts for the needy. Now let me carry the sack to your house."

As soon as the stranger had gone, Mordecai called his daughter Rachel to help him divide the foods into the usual three equal parts. But when they removed the top layer, they discovered the gold underneath. They were dumbfounded.

Finally, Mordecai found his tongue. "The stranger must have left his gold in the sack by mistake," he said. "I must return it to him right after the Sabbath."

Then he remembered his Friday mission. "The poor!" he exclaimed. "We have the stranger's gold, but we have no food for the needy! What shall we do?"

Mordecai realized that for the first time in his life he must disappoint those who expected his help. Suddenly he had an idea.

"Daughter," he said. "We will distribute our own food so that the poor won't go hungry. We can't disappoint them."

Rachel consented. They took their own food and distributed it among as many people as they possibly could in time for the Sabbath. Throughout that Sabbath, though they both went hungry, they were happy.

As soon as the Sabbath was over, Mordecai took the bag of gold to the market place. There he found the mysterious stranger.

"Yesterday," Mordecai said, "you forgot your gold in my charity-sack and I've brought it back to you."

Elijah replied: "Forgive me, my good man, but I

don't know what you're talking about. Whatever you found in the bag was sent by God for the poor you have fed all these years. The gold doesn't belong to me. It is a gift, and it belongs to them."

Puzzled, Mordecai walked slowly home. If this gold belongs to the poor, he thought, the Sabbath food I gave them was a small gift indeed. I must make amends.

As soon as he reached home, Mordecai divided the gold into three parts. That very night he distributed it among the widows, orphans, and students.

A week later, when the old man was out on his Friday mission as usual, he once again met the stranger in the market place. Elijah approached Mordecai with a warm smile and said: "Give me your bag again! This time divide the contents into four parts. The fourth part is for you alone."

Elijah filled the bag with precious stones. "Mordecai," he said, "you have given of yourself with a full heart all your life, and so the Lord rewards you with a full measure."

And saying that, Elijah the prophet disappeared.

From Jewish Folklore

The "Lion" and the Locusts

Rabbi Isaac Lurie was a great Jewish visionary and seer. He lived five hundred years ago in the ancient city of Safed. Here, in the hills of Galilee, Rabbi Isaac Lurie laid the foundations for the Jewish system of philosophy and mysticism known as the Kabbalah. His influence on Jewish learning was so great, his saintliness and scholarship were so widely esteemed, that his disciples came to call him the Ari Ha-Kadosh—the "Holy Lion"—in tribute to the power and majesty of his teachings.

Often Rabbi Isaac bypassed the classroom methods of teaching and took his students and disciples on long walks through the hills and valleys of Galilee. It was during these times that he spoke on the Torah and spread the teachings of the Kabbalah.

Many tales are told of the adventures that befell the Ari and his students during these walking lectures. One such story begins during a walk through a valley, while the Ari was expounding the mysteries of the Torah.

Suddenly, in the middle of a sentence, he came to an abrupt stop. He stood frozen, motionless, his eyes tightly shut, his face concentrating intensely on some inner emotional and spiritual experience. His companions sensed that something mystifying was taking place, so that they did not dare break his trance-like mood. They waited for him to speak to them.

But as time passed, and still the rabbi had not moved, or even seemed to take a breath, they wondered if he was hearing something which they could not hear.

For almost an hour the Ari kept this intense and motionless attitude. Then with a sudden, violent gesture, he thrust out his arm, his hand open, and cried out in one word:

"Money!"

The Ari was the most unworldly of men. His request startled his students. But unhesitatingly they searched their pockets for every coin they had, and placed them all in his hand.

"More!" commanded the Ari.

His disciples had no money left. But they proceeded to collect everything of value they had with them except for the clothes they wore. They implored the Ari to tell them why he needed the money.

This is what the Ari replied: "While I was speaking to you of the Torah, I heard a piercing, heart-rending cry. I paused to listen, and I saw a poor man in an attic in Safed weeping desperately. His poverty had made him bitter, and he was complaining to God. His cries and sobs penetrated the skies and reached the Heavenly Throne, whereupon it was decreed from on high: 'The town of Safed, once the pride and joy of the people of Israel, no longer deserves to live. It has allowed a poor man to live in extreme poverty within its gates, and in punishment the town must be destroyed. For its lack of mercy, a plague of locusts will descend on Safed, and it shall be utterly destroyed.' "

The Ari turned to one of his disciples, whose name was Jacob. "Therefore," he said to Jacob, "take this money and run as fast as you can to the lane of the beggars in Safed. There, in an attic above the house of Joseph the sweeper, you will find the man of whom I speak. Give this money to him. And, Jacob, I beg you to ask the man humbly and contritely to forgive us all for our neglect and delay."

Spurred by the Ari's urgency, Jacob dashed off and soon found the poor man weeping in the attic. Comforting the man, Jacob asked him why he was crying.

"My tears are forced from me," replied the man. "God has unjustly punished me. One misfortune after another follows me. I am naked and penniless. All I had left of all my former possessions was a single small jar, and this I took to the market place in order to sell it for a few pennies so that I could buy a few pieces of bread. But just as I was about to enter the market place, God caused me to stumble. The jar flew from my hands and was shattered on the ground. Now there is nothing left for me but to die a miserable death of starvation. And you ask me why I weep?"

Jacob thrust the money into the poor man's hands. "Here. Weep no more. Go and buy food and clothing. Live. And pray to forgive us. I beseech you to forgive us for our delay and neglect, and for the sufferings which we have caused you through them."

The light of renewed hope shone in the poor man's eyes. "But there is nothing to forgive. On the contrary, I give thanks to you and to my unknown benefactors who have delivered me from death. And Thee, O God," he continued, raising his eyes to Heaven, "I thank Thee for having heeded my prayer."

"Amen," replied Jacob, and he likewise raised his eyes to Heaven to pray.

Now as the two men raised their eyes to the skies, they saw a dark cloud in the distance. It grew rapidly larger as it moved swiftly toward the town. Others in the street outside had also seen the cloud. Now all stood watching fearfully as it approached. While it was yet some distance away, the people of Safed recognized the cloud for what it was—not the threat of rain but a swarm of locusts. On all sides the dread cry was taken up:

"Locusts! Locusts!"

Frantically, the people barricaded themselves in their houses, closing their doors and shutters. The sur-

rounding fields and orchards and gardens were doomed. The locusts would devour every green and growing thing. But at least the locusts could be kept out of their homes. A great sadness and despair settled over Safed. The people resigned themselves to destruction and starvation, and from every home came wails of mourning.

Up from the south came the locust swarm, flying directly toward Safed. Larger and larger it grew. It blotted out the sun, and darkened the skies. The enormous shadow of the swarm lay like a cloak over the hills of Galilee. Individual locusts were already in the town, already settling on the trees and gardens and already stripping away the leaves. In a few moments the main body of the swarm would arrive and all in town would be lost. The wails of the townspeople grew louder.

Suddenly, on the very edge of Safed, the swarm was seen to veer sharply to the west. A gale wind came up, deflecting the swarm from its course. Due west it was carried by the sudden gale, which swept it out to the Mediterranean Sea. Once the entire swarm was out over the sea, the gale died down, and the swarm of locusts sank below the waves.

The town of Safed was saved by the Holy Ari's perception of the Heavenly Decree, and his quick action in providing charity where charity was needed.

Simhah Assaf—Legends of Safed

The Beggar's Blessing

IN JERUSALEM many centuries ago the prophet Elijah would wander about the streets disguised as a beggar, observing the people without being recognized.

One day Elijah paused, hot, thirsty, and tired, before a large mansion. It was the house of Jabez, a master weaver, known to all as a greedy, hard-hearted man. Jabez shared his wealth with no one, not even his younger and only brother Simcha, who was a poor stonecutter.

When Elijah knocked upon the door, Jabez thrust his head out of the window. When he saw only a beggar, he seized a basin of water and flung it down.

The basin fell and shattered on the pavement, missing the beggar entirely. Jabez watched in amazement while Elijah calmly turned and walked on.

Soon Elijah saw a dingy little house at the roadside. This was the house of Simcha, who was as generous and kind as his brother was greedy and cruel. Simcha said, "Come in. Let me bathe your feet. My wife, Rivkah, will bring you some bread and dates."

When Elijah was ready to leave he turned to his hosts with a smile. "May God reward you," he said. "The first thing you wish to do will be blessed, and may you go on doing it until you cry 'Enough!'"

In an instant, Elijah had disappeared.

"He must have been one of God's angels," Rivkah said, then she cried out, "Simcha! Let us count our money—you heard what the blessed one said!"

Simcha's face fell. "But we have no money."

"Then run and borrow from your brother Jabez."

Simcha, listening to the advice of Rivkah, went to his well-to-do brother Jabez, and told him the story. Jabez was filled with envy. He agreed to lend Simcha a gold coin on one condition—that Simcha should pray to the beggar for the same chance for Jabez. Simcha gladly agreed, for he did not begrudge Jabez the same good fortune. Simcha ran home. There, while Rivkah watched, he set it on the table and called out:

"May I continue counting the gold until I cry *Enough!* One! Two! Three!"

Three gold coins glittered on the table where one had been before.

"Four! Five! Six! Seven!" The pile grew larger— and larger—and larger. Another man seeing the miracle, might have gone on counting for days and weeks; but Simcha was not greedy.

"*Enough!*" he cried finally, and the money stopped multiplying. Three-quarters of the gold Simcha put away to provide for his children. The rest he gave to Rivkah for their present needs. Then Simcha began to pray to the beggar to help Jabez.

Meanwhile, in order to be certain not to miss the mysterious beggar, Jabez was forced to throw his house open to every poor man who passed.

At last, Jabez saw the beggar he had been looking for. He begged him to enter and refresh himself.

Inside the house, Jabez's servants led the beggar to a soft couch. They washed his feet with rosewater, and set the finest foods and the rarest wines before him.

Now Jabez hastily ordered the servants to bar the

doors. After all, he thought, I have the one I'm looking for, and there's no sense wasting food and money on the others.

After Elijah had eaten and rested, Jabez waited for the granting of his wish.

And, indeed, Elijah did grant Jabez a wish. "May there be such a blessing on the next thing you do, that you shall do it forever."

Jabez was overjoyed. When Elijah was gone, he turned to his wife.

"Quick! We must count our gold at once! But first close the shutters and lock the doors; no one must see how rich we are becoming!"

And so Jabez and his wife rushed all through the house, slamming doors, closing windows, barring shutters. But then something strange happened: they could not stop what they were doing. Their hands went on opening doors and closing them, opening windows and closing them, opening shutters and slamming them shut again.

Thus had the beggar's parting words come true!

When Simcha came to Jabez's house, he found the front door locked. Inside he could see his brother and sister-in-law wearily closing windows and slamming the shutters, over and over.

Jabez gasped out the story of what had happened. "I've learned my lesson," he cried. "Oh, if only God would end this curse I swear I'll be generous to the end of my days!"

Simcha began at once to pray that Jabez and his wife might be given a chance to live a pious life. Finally Elijah heard his prayer and granted it.

Soon Jabez's house became as well known as his brother's for its hospitality and charity. In fact, their names became a byword in the land; parents blessed their children with the words, "May you too become as rich and as generous as Jabez and Simcha."

Jewish Folk Tale

Brothers All

THE Moslem Sabbath day is on Friday; the Christian Sabbath day is on Sunday; and the Jewish Sabbath day is on Saturday.

Now it happened in a small village in the Land of Israel that Mohammed the Moslem, Peter the Christian, and Aaron the Jew were the best of friends. Each of them observed his own Sabbath day.

One autumn Friday, Aaron and Peter set out to work their fields while Mohammed stayed home to observe his day of rest. As Aaron worked his own field he noticed that Mohammed's field was only half plowed. A thought came to him: since Mohammed can do no work today, and since it might rain tomorrow, my good friend's field may not be plowed in time for sowing the grain. Why don't I plow his field a little? That will make his work easier and perhaps save his crop this year.

While Aaron was thinking this, strangely enough, Peter had much the same thought as he plowed his own field. Without saying a word to each other, each of the men began to plow Mohammed's field at the same time— one from the east, the other from the west. Between them, they finished the entire field.

The next day Mohammed came out to work his field and found it all plowed. Marveling, he said, "I didn't finish plowing my field, yet it is all plowed. Surely, God sent his angels to plow my field while I observed His day of rest."

Months passed, the winter was over, and spring

came. The crops in the fields of the three friends flour-
ished, and the harvest season arrived. One Sunday morning Aaron and Mohammed were out in their fields,
while Peter stayed at home to observe his Sabbath. When
Aaron noticed Peter's field, he saw that the corn was full
and ready to cut. And once again he had the same
thought about Peter's field that he had had about Mohammed's field.

Strangely enough, while that thought was going on in Aaron's mind, a similar thought raced through Mohammed's mind. And so, unseen by each other, Aaron and Mohammed set to work to harvest Peter's corn—one from the north and the other from the south. Soon the entire crop was harvested.

The following day Peter went to his field to cut his corn, but found it all harvested. He raised his hands to heaven and said, "Surely God has sent his angels to labor in my fields and cut my corn for me."

Harvest time finally passed, and the threshing season arrived. One Saturday morning Mohammed and Peter went to their fields to thresh their grain while Aaron stayed at home, remembering the Sabbath day "to keep it holy."

Now as Mohammed glanced up at the sky, where clouds were gathering, he thought: Today is Saturday, Aaron's Sabbath. He cannot work in his field. But the rain is coming. It will wash his grain away and he'll lose his crop. I'll ask Peter to help me thresh Aaron's grain, and we'll save it for Aaron.

The two men worked to save Aaron's grain, threshing it and binding it and covering it with straw to protect it from the coming rain.

The next day, when Aaron came to his field, he found his grain already threshed and safe under the straw. Lifting his eyes up to heaven, he said, "Blessed art Thou, O Lord, who dost send Thy angels to help those who remember Thy Sabbath Day 'to keep it holy'!"

Retold by A. E.

The Weight of Charity

Aaron had always done his best to live up to the Jewish code of ethics. He had observed the *Mitzvot,* studied Torah, been active in Jewish affairs, and raised his family in the Jewish tradition.

Most important of all, Aaron had helped the needy. Therefore, when it was Aaron's time to die, he faced "Judgment Day" calmly.

But then his soul discovered that even the bravest cannot be calm in the face of Eternity. And when an angel approached Aaron, he, too, was frightened.

The angel led him to a doorway. "Behind this door," he said, "the people of your town are judged. Come, let us enter." "All right," said Aaron shakily.

Opening the door, the angel led Aaron down a corridor, from which many doors opened into small cells. The angel stopped. "This is your cell," he said. Behind an open door stood the Weighing Angel, with a pair of empty scales in his hand.

"Are you ready?" the Weighing Angel asked.

"Yes," whispered Aaron.

"Good," said the Weighing Angel. "First we will weigh your acts relating to the study of Torah." He picked up a large slab of silver and laid it on the scales. The pan sank down. The other pan rose high in the air.

The Guiding Angel explained, "The slab of silver represents the weight of an average man's devotion to Torah. Now you will see whether your *Mitzvot* in Torah study were average or not."

Aaron watched while the empty pan sank and the pan with the silver slab rose slowly.

The Guiding Angel, smiling, said: "Your *Mitzvot* on earth are not visible. Still, as you can see, they are being added to the scale."

And indeed Aaron could see the Torah pan steadily sink as his earthly hours of study were added to it. The two pans drew level and for a moment they hovered, perfectly balanced. Then the "empty" pan continued its downward motion. Aaron sighed in relief.

"Now," the Guiding Angel said, "your acts of worship and prayer will be weighed."

After that came Aaron's communal activity. And again and again his *Mitzvot* were weighed. On the whole Aaron was not displeased.

"And now at last," said the Guiding Angel, "your charity."

The Weighing Angel laid aside the silver slab and picked up a much heavier ingot of gold.

"Charity," explained the Guiding Angel, "is by far the most important of all the *Mitzvot*. It is worth its weight in gold."

Aaron's heart sank. His deeds until now had shown only a slightly better than average record when weighed against the silver bar. But what chance would he have against the heavier gold one? He had never been a rich man. It had always been a struggle to make a living. He had never been able to spare very much for charity.

He turned to the Guiding Angel and said, "Does Heaven abide by the rules of the Talmud? Or were they intended only for human conduct and is the Heavenly Court exempt from them?"

The Angel replied, "The sages of the Talmud taught the truth. And the truth is the same everywhere, in Heaven as on earth."

Depressed more than ever, Aaron said to the Angel, "I have been thinking of a talmudic teaching. Rabbi Assi taught: 'Charity is as weighty as all the other *Mitzvot* in the Torah combined.' If Rabbi Assi is right . . ." He left the thought unfinished.

"Well," said the Angel, "let us see what the scales will show."

The Weighing Angel placed the heavy ingot of gold on the scales. The empty pan rose high while Aaron looked on hopelessly.

But as he watched, the pan with the gold began slowly to rise. Incredulously Aaron saw the pans approach each other. Soon they were exactly level. Then up, up went the gold; down, down went the "empty" pan, until it could go no further.

"There must be some mistake!" cried Aaron.

The Weighing Angel showed Aaron the charity records of all the townsmen who had preceded him. Not one was as good.

Aaron was astounded. "I *know* many of these men gave far more than I did to charity."

"Aaron," the Guiding Angel said, "charity is not like the other *Mitzvot*. The amount of charity a man gives depends on his means, and is proportionate. It is true that many gave far more than you did, but none gave so much out of so little.

"For you, therefore," continued the Angel, "a special place is reserved in Heaven. Look there!"

Stunned, Aaron raised his eyes and saw two figures —Abraham and Rabbi Assi.

"Together with Abraham, father of hospitality and with Rabbi Assi, who taught the true meaning of charity," said the Angel, "you will enjoy the Eternal reward."

And so the happy soul of Aaron joined the souls of Abraham and Rabbi Assi for all time.

Moses Eskolsky

The Pride of the Beggars

THIS happened many years ago when a great rabbi, arriving in the Holy Land, embarked on his first pilgrimage to the Wailing Wall in Jerusalem.

Along the edge of the pavement he saw scores of beggars lined up, holding their cups out before them, pleading for a coin. By their expressions and the wail in their voices, the rabbi felt that they were all ashamed of their calling.

It was then that a thought came to the rabbi. He stopped before the first beggar, a Persian, and held his hand out in greeting.

"*Shalom Aleichem!*" he said.

The beggar was startled to be greeted so cordially, especially by a man who was obviously a great scholar. But he proved to be equal to the occasion.

"*Aleichem ha-Shalom,*" he replied, and firmly grasped the hand held out to him in greeting.

Humbly, the rabbi asked: "Will you do me the honor and favor of allowing me to drop a coin in your cup?"

The Persian beggar was thunderstruck. No one had ever approached him in this manner. The great and honored rabbi was asking *him* for permission to give him charity! He could not understand it. But once again he rose to the moment. With a careful grace he courteously motioned toward his beggar's cup and murmured, "With pleasure; the honor is mine."

The rabbi dropped a large coin into the cup and again shook the beggar's hand, thanking him for his

courtesy and his kindness, and taking ceremonious leave of him.

Slowly the rabbi continued on his way, stopping before each beggar and exchanging a few words with each, then extending his alms with an air of gratitude for a favor received rather than conferred. Nothing of this kind had ever happened before, and the beggars could not understand it.

The rabbi finally reached the Wailing Wall, thanked God for allowing him to pay homage at the last vestige of the ancient Temple, and then turned to leave.

At that moment one of the bolder beggars, gathering together enough courage, approached the rabbi.

"Please forgive me for asking, Rabbi," he said. "For many years we have sat here and no one has ever behaved in this way. I am sure there must be some significance to your words and actions. Please explain them to us."

The rabbi stood silent for a long moment, lost in thought. Then he asked the beggar a question.

"Why do you sit asking for alms here near the Wall and not somewhere else?"

"Because people who are on their way to the Wall feel more inclined to give alms," replied the beggar.

"Exactly," said the rabbi. "Now I will answer your question. All my life in the *Galut* I have prayed for Jerusalem, thought about Jerusalem, longed for Jerusalem. In the center of all my thoughts about Jerusalem was the Wailing Wall, the one visible relic of the ancient Temple which was the crowning glory of the people of Israel thousands of years ago. All my life I have waited for the moment when I could pray directly to God at the site of His House. Only last night I reached the Holy Land, and I immediately made my way to Jerusalem. This morning when I set out for the Wall I knew how I would pray to God when I reached it, but I had no way of knowing how acceptable my prayers would be. Now when I saw you, the beggars, I realized that God had sent me a way of insuring that my prayers would be acceptable. It was not I who did you a favor by giving you alms. It was *you* who did *me* a favor by accepting alms from me, making it possible for me to perform an act of charity. By doing this you opened the Gates of Heaven for my prayers at the Wall. For this I was grateful, as should everyone be who enjoys the privilege of giving alms to you just before he prays at the House of God. You are the men who hold in your hands the keys to the Gates of Heaven. You should be the proudest men in Jerusalem."

From that day on, beggars at the Wailing Wall in Jerusalem were not like beggars elsewhere in the world. They were not downcast, they were not crestfallen as beggars usually are. There was nothing sheepish or shamefaced about them. They practiced their art with a flourish, proud to accept alms from worshiping pilgrims, and cheerfully bestowing a blessing upon the person who gave them alms.

Moses Eskolsky

STORIES FROM
THE RECENT PAST

INTRODUCTION—*Give of Yourself*

GREAT and noble is *Tzedakah*—the Jewish idea of charity, justice and mercy. But *Gemilut Hasadim* is even greater. Both are expressions for charity but with different meanings. As we said at the beginning, *Tzedakah* is hard to translate, *Gemilut Hasadim* is even harder. We usually call it "loving-kindness," but it means many things: love, grace, concern, personal service—for the ill, for the orphan, for the rich as well as for the poor, for the happy as well as for the unhappy.

"On three things the world rests," the Rabbis taught: "on the Study of Torah, on Prayer and on *Gemilut Hasadim*." The Rabbis further say that *Gemilut Hasadim* is greater than *Tzedakah* in three ways: *Tzedakah* we do with our money, *Gemilut Hasadim* we do with our hearts, our own personal care; *Tzedakah* we give to the needy, *Gemilut Hasadim* we give to all;

Tzedakah we do for the living, *Gemilut Hasadim* we do for the living *and* the dead (by accompanying them to their final resting place, taking part in their burial and honoring their memory). Indeed, the Rabbis point out that the Five Books of Moses begin and end with acts of *Gemilut Hasadim* performed by the Lord Himself when He sewed leaves to clothe Adam and Eve and when He buried Moses.

This great ideal of personal service shone bright in the lives of our sages. Our leaders of the recent past (and of modern times) are remembered not so much because they were the "people of the book," scholars and learned men but because of their humaneness. The warmth of their personalities was richer than the words of their teaching. What they were was greater than what they said; what they did inspired more than what they taught. Their daily deeds, reflecting the teaching of the Law which they absorbed in their hearts and minds, were a continuous divine service to God and man.

In this final section we present incidents in the lives of some of our rabbis of the recent past whose greatness lies not only in their scholarship and teachings, but also in their everyday performance of good deeds arising from their hearts. Despite their profound learning they humbly, devotedly and selflessly served the common man. And in so doing they became walking examples of *Gemilut Hasadim,* living inspirations to their generation and for many generations to come.

The Greatest Commandment

IN KOVNO, where Rabbi Israel Salanter lived for a time, there was a home for beggars and anyone else who could not afford a night's lodging. It was a disgrace—neglected, broken-down and filthy. Lodgers lived amid dirt and disorder. And the trustees closed their eyes to the horrible conditions there. They never bothered to repair, or clean or improve the place in any way.

That is, until Rabbi Israel heard about this home. One evening, after synagogue, he went there himself, and slept there all night, on the bare floor, in the filth, along with the others.

The next morning, when people saw the famous rabbi coming from the home, the shocking news spread like fire through the town.

That very day, the trustees began to clean up the home. Otherwise, they explained, how could they face the rabbi?

This was generally the way people reacted in the presence of Rabbi Israel. He was known far and wide as a great and learned rabbi, strict and pious about all God's commandments, and especially about the greatest commandment of all—*Tzedakah*.

Once, just before Passover, the rabbi became ill. He was responsible for supervising all Passover laws, and especially the baking of *Matzot*. His students knew how strict he was about it, how carefully he examined the flour, the dough, every step of the baking process. And so, when Rabbi Israel asked his students to supervise the baking of *Matzot* for him, they felt deeply honored. Before they left his bedside, one of the students asked: "Rabbi, what should we watch for especially?"

"The woman who does the kneading of the dough," Rabbi Israel replied with difficulty. "Be particularly careful when you supervise her."

"Certainly, Rabbi. But what does she do that's wrong?"

Rabbi Israel forced himself up on one elbow. "Never mind her!" he cried. "It's *you* who must be careful. Do not inspect her work too carefully. Don't say or do *anything* that might offend her. Overlook any mistake she makes. The poor woman is a widow!"

He fell back on his pillow, and the students trooped out, somewhat shamefaced at their own pride and self-importance in contrast with the problems that were important to Rabbi Israel.

Another time, Rabbi Israel's students brought him water to wash his hands before mealtime. The pail was full, and they filled a cup for him. But, oddly enough, the rabbi put only a drop or two on his hands. The students were left speechless. Their beloved rabbi, the most pious Jew of his generation, skimping on the commandment to wash thoroughly before eating?

Hesitantly, one of the students addressed him: "We cannot understand why you used so little water, Rabbi. Not enough, really, to wash your hands."

Rabbi Israel pointed out the window. They looked and saw a servant girl coming up the path from the well. She was bent low under the heavy bar laid across her shoulders, from each end of which hung an overflowing pail of water.

"My sons," explained Rabbi Israel, "how could I perform any commandment at the expense of this poor girl's shoulders? The water I saved may help prevent one trip to the well for her. *You* can save her even more!"

The students were silent, realizing that Rabbi Israel was showing them the true meaning of *Tzedakah*. They could only hope that they, too, would be able to perform the invisible acts of Charity—the greatest commandment of all.

Jewish Folk Tale

Even Higher

EVERY morning during the Days of Penitence, the *Rebbi* of Nemirov would disappear. The members of his family would arise early for *Selihot* and go to the synagogue. Undoubtedly he left the house after them. But no one ever saw him, either in the street, or in the main synagogue, or in the *Bet Ha-Midrash,* or in any of the small congregations. As for his house being left wide open, no one worried about it. Thieves would not dare trespass the *Rebbi's* house. One touch of the doorknob and the thief's hand would wither.

But where did the *Rebbi* vanish?—all asked. Where else, but into heaven? Certainly he had many urgent matters to take care of. The High Holy Day season is here. The needs of Israel are many. Jews need to earn a living. They need peace and health. The Day of Judgment is at hand. Satan is as alert as ever, diligently looking for sins. He looks into the heart, into the innermost recesses of the soul. He is busy getting people to sin. And when they do, Satan goes right up to high heaven and accuses them before the Supreme Judge. Who will plead their case, if not the holy one of Nemirov? And so he ascends every year to intercede with the Heavenly Throne for his people, Israel.

One day, there came to Nemirov a *Mitnaged,* a *Litvak*—from Vilna, the Jerusalem of Lithuania, no less. He jeered at the belief of the townsfolk. As is well known, the strength of the Lithuanians lies in their logic. They are dry, matter-of-fact. They have no imagination, no faith in the supernatural powers of the *Rebbi*. Our *Litvak* scoffed at the townspeople and cited chapter and verse from the Talmud to prove that even Moses never really ascended to heaven, but remained at a certain distance below. And if this was so in the case of Moses, how much more so in the case of the *Rebbi* of Nemirov?

"Very well, smartie!" retorted the townsmen. "Where then is the *Rebbi* during the *Selihot?*"

The Lithuanian answered drily that he had a list of more important questions that begged for answers. Nevertheless, he made up his mind to investigate and get to the bottom of this matter.

That very day at twilight, between *Minhah* and *Maariv* services, the Lithuanian stole into the *Rebbi's* bedroom and crept under his bed. Being a *Litvak*, he naturally had supreme confidence in his ability to stay awake through the long hours. To keep awake, he selected various portions of the Talmud and reviewed them from memory.

An hour before the *Shammash* called for *Selihot,* the Lithuanian heard the *Rebbi* stirring. He heard him sigh and groan. Now, it is well known that the *Rebbi's* sighs were filled with sorrow, pain, and anguish. All who heard them melted with grief. But not our Lithuanian. He did not stop from his silent study even for a moment.

And when the *Shammash* rapped for *Selihot,* the Lithuanian heard the commotion in the other rooms. People got out of bed, lit candles, washed their hands, dressed, walked about, opened doors. Finally quiet was restored, and the light disappeared from under the doors of the nearby rooms. The two remained alone.

Later, the Lithuanian openly confessed that when he was left alone with the *Rebbi,* a great fear seized him. To be alone with the *Rebbi* during *Selihot* time is not a thing to take lightly. But the Lithuanian was stubborn. He was trembling all over; nevertheless, he remained hidden in the *Rebbi's* bedroom.

Soon the *Rebbi* arose. He got out of bed and went over to the wardrobe and took out a bundle of clothing. The clothes were those of a peasant—wide, short linen trousers; high boots, smeared with pitch; a knee-length heavy coat; a high fur cap; and a leather belt, set with brass studs. These the *Rebbi* put on. From the pocket of his coat dangled the end of a thick rope.

The Lithuanian could not believe his eyes. He pinched himself to make sure he was not dreaming. The *Rebbi* went out of his room, with the Lithuanian following stealthily behind him. The *Rebbi* went to the kitchen, and from under the cook's bed took out an ax. He stuck it under his belt and left the house. The Lithuanian followed him. Truthfully, for a moment the incredible thought occurred to him that the *Rebbi* led a double life, a saint by day and a robber by night.

Outside, the solemn spirit of the High Holy Day season prevailed. Every now and then came the moan of a sick person or the mournful chant of *Selihot.* The *Rebbi* glided along silently, hugging the shadows of the houses. He seemed to dissolve in the dark and reappear suddenly in the light of the moon. The Lithuanian kept after him, his heart pounding as if it were echoing the footsteps of the *Rebbi.*

Soon the *Rebbi* passed the outskirts of the town. Near the town was a dense wood. The *Rebbi* entered the wood, went up to a young oak tree, pulled the ax from his belt, and proceeded to chop it down.

The Lithuanian stood at a distance and watched the *Rebbi* chop the tree into logs and the logs into kindling wood. Then he saw him take out the rope from his coat pocket, tie it around a bundle of kindling wood, heave the bundle over his shoulders, and retrace his steps. Bowed under his load, the *Rebbi* walked back to the town. The Lithuanian followed, wondering whether the *Rebbi* was in his right mind.

The *Rebbi* kept a straight course. Soon he came to a dark alley and stopped before a broken-down hut. He went to the window and knocked gently on the pane. From inside the house came the weak voice of a sick woman.

"Who is there?"

"I," answered the *Rebbi* in Russian.

The woman persisted, "Who is *I*?"

The *Rebbi* replied, "Vassil."

"Vassil? Which Vassil? And what do you want?"

The *Rebbi* replied in Russian, as before, that he had a bundle of kindling wood for sale, and that he would sell it cheaply. He did not wait for an answer, but opened the door and entered the house. The Lithuanian stole in behind him.

In the pale light of the silvery moon the Lithuanian saw a tiny low-ceilinged room, with a few rickety pieces of furniture. A sick woman covered with rags lay on a bed. With a sigh she asked: "How can I pay you? I am a penniless widow."

The *Rebbi* replied, "I trust you. The entire bundle costs only six cents."

"I can't afford it even if you trust me. I don't see where I can get the money to pay you later. I'm poor and helpless."

Meanwhile the *Rebbi* had already put down the bundle on the floor. Pretending anger, he retorted, "Foolish woman! I trust you with six cents' worth of kindling wood. You have a great and eternal God, and yet you don't have enough faith in Him that some day He'll provide you with six cents to pay your loan."

"And who will light the oven for me? Who knows when my son will return from work?"

"I'll do it for you," answered the *Rebbi.*

He set to work. When he put the wood into the oven, he quietly chanted the first part of the *Selihot.* When he kindled the wood, he chanted the second part, and when he closed the oven on the crackling fire, he chanted merrily the last part.

This incident caused a change in the Lithuanian. He became an ardent admirer and a devoted follower of the *Rebbi.* He visited him twice every year, and when the *Hasidim* talked of the *Rebbi's* miraculous ascent to heaven during *Selihot,* he did not scoff, but added reverently: "Who knows? Maybe even higher!"

Isaac Leib Peretz

The Baby Sitter

I<small>T WAS</small> Yom Kippur Eve, the most solemn hour of the year. Silent, reverent worshipers wait in the synagogue for the cantor to chant the most solemn prayer, *Kol Nidre*. Prayer-shawls cover their heads; the cantor and the choir stand ready. Outside, the sun is setting. Inside the synagogue, wax candles splutter and crackle.

But something is wrong. Their beloved Rabbi Israel Salanter has not yet arrived. Usually he is among the first in the synagogue. His delay is causing a great deal of anxiety. The trustees look out through the door, but see only the gathering shadows. They send the sexton to the rabbi's home, but he returns with the news that the rabbi's house is locked and empty.

Fear and dread grip the congregation. On this most important night of all nights of the year, where has the rabbi gone to? What can have happened to him? Has Satan trapped him in his net? Have the angels called him to heaven to plead for his people? Is he lying somewhere, hurt or sick?

This is what actually happened:

Rabbi Salanter had left for the synagogue in plenty of time. But as he was passing a small house at the end of a street, he heard the sounds of an infant wailing and a child's voice calling out: "God help me! Tell me what to do!"

As fast as he was able to, the rabbi rushed into the house and found a little girl rocking her baby brother. The infant was screaming its lungs out.

Anxiously, the rabbi asked, "What is it, child?"

"My baby brother," sobbed the girl. "My father and mother went to the synagogue and I'm watching the baby. But he woke up and he's crying and I don't know how to stop him."

Rabbi Salanter sighed with relief. He smiled gently as he took the baby from her. "Run and bring your mother," he said. "I'll take care of the baby."

Thankfully, the girl dashed off. But in the synagogue everyone was so upset over the missing rabbi that they never noticed the child who climbed up to the women's section, whispered to one of the women, and hurried out with her.

When the mother entered her home she saw old Rabbi Israel Salanter singing softly to the baby the *Kol Nidre* chant: "And the Congregation of Israel shall be forgiven . . ."

The child was lying peacefully in the rabbi's arms.

Giving the baby to its mother, Rabbi Salanter left without a further word.

On his arrival at the synagogue everyone, relieved that their rabbi seemed all right, crowded around him and asked him what happened to delay him.

The rabbi smiles. "There were these innocent children crying for help," he explains. "And there was I— so *Kol Nidre* had to wait. I'm sorry, but it's never too late for us to ask God to help *us*. He will listen to *Kol Nidre* even if we are a little late."

The rabbi takes his place, the cantor and the choir lift up their voices, and the congregation worships.

Truly, God seems close, listening, ready to help.

Jewish Folk Tale

A Poor Memory

IN THE town of Salant lived Rabbi Sundell, teacher of the famous Rabbi Israel Salanter. Rabbi Sundell was a champion of the poor and needy, and he would often go out of his way to help them no matter how difficult or embarrassing the situation might be for himself. It was said of Rabbi Sundell that he would willingly face the torture rack if it meant relief for the poor and unfortunate. And as for facing the wrath of a wealthy giver . . .

One day Rabbi Sundell heard that a certain rich man had refused to help a distant relative who had fallen into poverty. Without thinking twice about the matter, the rabbi paid a visit to the rich man. He was greeted with respect befitting his position and scholarship.

After some moments of conversation, Rabbi Sundell said to his host, "Do you pray every day, my friend?"

The rich man stiffened. "Does the rabbi doubt my piety?"

Rabbi Sundell shook his head.

"Of course I pray every day. Three times!"

"In that case," said the rabbi, paying no attention to the man's hurt manner, "can you repeat the beginning of the Eighteen Benedictions—the *Shemoneh Esreh?*"

A quick anger flashed across the rich man's face, but he controlled himself in the next moment. "Does the rabbi think I'm a baby? Any child knows the *Shemoneh Esreh* begins, 'Blessed art Thou, O Lord our God and the God of our fathers, the God of Abraham, the God of Isaac, and the God of Jacob . . .'"

The rabbi stopped him with a gesture. "But do you also know when these fathers of ours actually lived?"

The man looked puzzled and irritated. "Everyone knows they lived thousands of years ago."

"Where?"

The rich man exploded. "I must say, Rabbi, if you weren't the . . ." He stopped. Red-faced, he went on: "They lived in our holy land, *Eretz Yisrael*."

Rabbi Sundell nodded. "You are well informed. And you have an excellent memory. Our forefathers lived thousands of years ago, far off in *Eretz Yisrael*. Yet you remember them three times every day in your prayers. And in your prayers, you hope the good Lord will remember *you* for health and prosperity because you call to Him in their name."

"Is there anything wrong with that, Rabbi?"

The rabbi straightened up slowly, then said very slowly: "How do you find it so difficult to remember a living man, a man who is your relative, who lives in this very city, and who needs your help?"

For a moment the rich man stood stock still, his mouth open and his eyes glazed. Then he bowed his head and said, "Forgive me, Rabbi. I have sinned."

Rabbi Sundell, his face glowing, answered, "We are all sinners, my son. And it is God who forgives—when we deserve it. Go now to the man you have remembered —and God be with you."

Jewish Folk Tale

The Broken Leg

THE congregation in Prague wanted a thrilling new explanation of the week's Torah reading—but Rabbi Ezekiel Landau spoke instead on the subject of *Tzedakah.*

The congregation wanted scholarly quotations—but Rabbi Ezekiel described the sufferings of the city's poor.

The congregation wanted brilliant deductions to explain difficult passages in the Bible—but Rabbi Ezekiel told them of starving families and shivering children.

Sabbath after Sabbath it went on this way—an appeal for help, for action, for funds, when the congregation wanted more and more learning. Finally the congregation became very tired of the whole thing, and began to murmur and make remarks. At last one of the trustees dropped a hint to Rabbi Ezekiel on the subject.

Two days later Rabbi Ezekiel came to the crowded, noisy market place of Prague to take his place among the merchants and peddlers. He had packs and boxes, which he calmly opened; he had goods and merchandise, which he smilingly spread out for buyers to see; he raised his voice just as the other merchants did, calling on the crowd to come see, come buy.

Everyone was shocked. Word of the rabbi's strange behavior spread rapidly, and soon a great crowd of merchants, shoppers, and passers-by milled around the rabbi, watching him carefully, passing him back and forth, but

always turning away from him with embarrassment when he happened to catch their eye.

One man nudged another, "Go and buy something from the rabbi. Ask him why he has turned merchant. Go call the trustees. Send for the rabbi's wife . . ."

Finally someone in the crowd called out loudly, "Rabbi! What are you doing here?"

The rabbi nodded pleasantly to the speaker, as if thanking him for asking. Then, putting down the merchandise, the rabbi climbed up on a box. A deep hush fell over the crowd.

"Jews! I have a three-legged stool," the rabbi said in a friendly and gracious tone. "The other day one of the legs broke off near the bottom. Naturally, I just propped it up with a block of wood and went right on using the stool."

The people stared at the rabbi, then at each other. Now they were more than ever convinced that something terrible had happened to their rabbi's mind.

"This morning," continued the rabbi, "a piece broke off from the edge of the *second* leg. Now I had *two* short legs, and it wouldn't be safe with *two* props— the stool would twist and anyone would fall off. So what did I do? I sawed off a piece of the third leg and made all three legs even. Now my stool stands straight and firm once again."

At this the crowd began to mutter, partly embarrassed and partly frightened by their rabbi's "madness." But Rabbi Ezekiel raised his hand, and now as his voice rang out it had a sharp edge to it: "We are taught, my friends, that the world rests on three things: on the Study of Torah, on Prayer, and on *Gemilut Hasadim*—

doing of kind deeds. When we lost our Temple, one of the three legs on which the world stands became shortened. But our wise men made a prop of it—the synagogue and the prayers of our lips. Now you of Prague have shortened a second leg—the leg of kind deeds. The world cannot stand firmly on *two* props, so the only thing left to do is cut down the *third* leg and make all three equal. Therefore, Jews, I have cut down on my study of Torah, and come to the market place instead. I am doing *my* part to keep the world balanced—at least," and here the rabbi smiled sadly, "I am helping to keep the city of Prague in balance!"

No one spoke. No one moved. Then, one by one, people turned and went about their business in silence.

In silence, too, Rabbi Ezekiel packed up his merchandise and went home.

On the next Sabbath, when Rabbi Ezekiel preached on *Tzedakah,* the congregation listened with respectful attention. After the service, man after man came up to shake his hand and to say: "Rabbi, how much do you want me to contribute? What can I do to help?"

Jewish Folk Tale

The Secret

NEW YORK's well-known orthodox rabbinical seminary is named after Rabbi Isaac Elchanan. When he lived in Kovno, Lithuania, the rabbi was a great scholar and was especially loved for his deeds of *Tzedakah*.

Once during a severe depression, Rabbi Isaac and one of his trustees went out collecting for a man who had lost all his wealth at one stroke. This man was well known and honored in the city, so the rabbi decided to keep his name a secret.

The rabbi and his trustee came to the home of a rich man from whom they expected a large sum. Their host greeted them kindly and made them comfortable. Then he asked the purpose of the rabbi's visit.

"We're here for a contribution," answered Rabbi Isaac.

"For community needs?" asked the host.

"For a certain person who is badly in need," replied the rabbi.

"Who is he?"

Rabbi Isaac shook his head. "We cannot reveal his name. He is a man who has suddenly found himself penniless and hungry. He'd be ashamed to have people know he was accepting charity."

The rich man looked from the rabbi to the trustee. His jaw hardened. "I want to know who it is," he insisted. "In fact—I was going to give you twenty-five rubles when you first mentioned a contribution, but I'll make it *fifty* rubles if you tell me his name."

"Sorry," the rabbi said firmly, shaking his head again. "We won't give away his name."

"A hundred rubles!" cried the rich man stubbornly. "Surely you're not going to refuse an amount like that!"

The trustee started to say something, but Rabbi Isaac cut in sharply: "The name is a secret! Give what you wish, but do not argue with me!"

The rich man took a deep breath, closed his eyes, and said, "Four hundred rubles!"

The trustee could not contain himself any longer. "Rabbi! Rabbi! Tell him! Four hundred rubles, Rabbi! We won't have to make another visit! Make him promise to keep it secret! But tell him, tell him!"

Rabbi Isaac stood up and reached for his coat. "I should not have listened to you even this far," he said to the host. "The honor of a man is greater than all the gold and silver in the world." He turned to the trustee. "Let us leave. We have many other visits to make."

But at these words the rich man seized the rabbi's arm and begged permission for a private word with him in the next room. When they were alone, the host suddenly broke down into tears.

"The truth is, Rabbi," he sobbed, "I'm bankrupt myself. I'm at the end of my rope. I can't give my own family food and shelter much longer. I wanted to come to you for help, but I couldn't stand the idea of everyone in Kovno hearing about my failure."

"Forgive me, my son," said Rabbi Isaac Elchanan gravely, "for not understanding your trouble. So you tested me to see if I would keep *Tzedakah* secret or not. Well, now you know. I will collect for you too, my son, and your name will never be mentioned."

The rabbi went back into the other room where the trustee was pacing up and down the floor.

"Well, Rabbi," the trustee asked excitedly, "how much? How much did he give you?"

Rabbi Isaac smiled. "It's a secret," he said.

Jewish Folk Tale

The Double-Box Mystery

MANY years ago in Berlin, Germany, two families named Gutman were at odds with each other. That is to say, the fathers of these families were angry at each other—and they were brothers. The other members of each family, respecting the wishes of the head of the household, went along with the feud, though often they tried—and failed—to bring the brothers together.

What had happened was that when the father of the Gutman brothers had died, he had left an equal sum of money to each of his sons. The older brother, Alfred, had wanted his younger brother, Carl, to go into business with him. But Carl, a teacher, did not care to give up teaching for business. This angered Alfred. A terrible argument followed and the brothers went their separate ways.

Years later, after both brothers had married and had children, and Alfred had grown wealthy while Carl grew poorer, there were attempts by family, by relatives, and even by friends to reconcile the two brothers. But Alfred would do nothing to help his brother, nor would Carl have accepted any help from Alfred.

Neither brother could understand that it was his own family that suffered the pain of an argument, the reason for which had almost been forgotten.

And then a strange thing happened. Both Alfred and Carl became ill, and died within a day of each other. And it was the Double-Box Mystery that at last brought the two families together.

Here is how it happened. For a hundred and fifty years the Jewish community of Berlin had supported a society to help mourners. This society was especially concerned about deaths in poor families, where the wage-earners of the family would have to lose a week's work in order to sit *Shivah* (the week of mourning), as required by Jewish law. The reason for the society's existence was to spare the feelings of needy people and not embarrass them by public help.

Therefore, at every death, regardless of whether the family was rich or poor, the society sent two locked boxes to the house of mourning. One box contained money intended for poor families. With this box there was a key in a sealed package and a letter asking the head of the house to break open the seal, unlock the box, and take out all the money. He was instructed to keep as much as he needed to help his family over the mourning period, and then to put the rest into the second box. If he did not need financial help he was to put *all* the money into the second box, and add a contribution of his own. Regardless of what he did with the money from the first box, he was to lock it up again, reseal the key, and return both boxes to the society.

The society would then fill up the first box again, and send both boxes to the next house where a death occurred. The second box was left untouched for months at a time, and as it passed from house to house it became heavier and heavier with contributions. From this box the society drew more funds to keep the first box filled.

Because the boxes went to *every* mourner, and the first box *always* came back empty, no one could tell

which mourner had kept the money or how much of it he had kept. No one could tell which mourner had replaced the money or how much he had added to it. No one was embarrassed by the arrival or departure of the boxes, since they "visited" every mourning household.

When the boxes came to Alfred Gutman's home, Alfred's wife did not need the money from the first box. She placed all of it in the second box. But she knew, too, that Carl was very ill and was not expected to live, so she added a large contribution of her own to the second box, resealed both boxes and returned them to the society.

The next day when Carl died, the society sent both boxes to Carl's home; and there Carl's wife, needing money, took a sum that would tide her family over the week of mourning. Somehow, too, she knew that Alfred's wife had provided a goodly sum of the money that was sealed in the first box.

Later, after the week of mourning, Carl's wife went to visit Alfred's wife. The two women looked at each other. They did not have to speak. They broke into tears, they embraced, and thus the two families were reunited.

Retold by A. E.

A Smile for a Heart

EVERYONE in Zanz knew Rabbi Hayim as a charitable and wise man. People were particularly delighted by his gentle sense of humor, which they said was capable of calming any emotional situation.

To prove this they told the story of when the rabbi's eldest daughter was to be wed. A few days before that event, a poor woman came to the rabbi and complained tearfully that her daughter was to be married and that she had no bridal clothes to give her.

Without a word, Rabbi Hayim took his own daughter's trousseau and gave it to the woman. Seeing this, the rabbi's eldest daughter cried out, "But what will I wear at my wedding, Father?"

"Don't worry," replied Rabbi Hayim gently. "Just tell the groom's family that you are my daughter."

As another example of Rabbi Hayim's generosity to the poor and needy, the people of Zanz used to tell the story of the rabbi's youngest daughter, who came to him one day and said, "Father, there is a wedding today. All the girls are to join in the bridal dance. I need new shoes."

But the rabbi replied, "Your old shoes will do."

A few minutes later the wife of a poor teacher came to him and sobbed out, "Oh Rabbi, there's to be a bridal dance and my daughter has no shoes."

Whereupon the rabbi, without a moment's hesitation, gave her money to buy shoes for her daughter.

A relative had witnessed both scenes and was

shocked. "How can you discriminate against your own daughter, Rabbi?"

Rabbi Hayim smiled and said, "The teacher's daughter comes from a family that is poor but proud. People would be more likely to make remarks if she wore old and torn shoes, and the remarks would hurt. But if my daughter wears old shoes, people will only say, 'How pious our rabbi is. He even allows his daughter to come to the bridal dance in old and torn shoes.'"

Jewish Folk Tale

Why the Rabbi Rode on Yom Kippur

THE Rabbi riding on Yom Kippur?

Rabbi Perlmutter, famous for his piety, riding on Yom Kippur through the streets of Warsaw?

A Jew, seeing this, turned pale with shock. He whispered the information to his companion, who whipped around toward him and said, "Nonsense! You must be blind! Hold your tongue!"

"But there he is in that streetcar!" insisted the first man. "I saw him getting on at the corner! Look!" And he pointed at a streetcar just about to leave the corner. "And his assistant is with him! On Yom Kippur, too!"

The companion looked into the streetcar, and his mouth fell open. Yes, it was white-bearded Rabbi Perlmutter, his white Yom Kippur *Kittel* and *Tallit* covered by his overcoat. He was sitting in the almost empty streetcar with his assistant. The two Jews looked at each other in horror.

The year was 1920. Poles were fighting Russians. Anyone discovered by the Polish authorities to be a communist was shot as a traitor. As the two men ran into the synagogue to report to the worshipers what they had seen, they found that the congregation was excited and bewildered. A few minutes earlier, in the middle of the sacred *Neilah* service, a message had been brought to Rabbi Perlmutter that a young Jew, a member of the congregation, had been arrested and was about to be executed as a Russian spy.

Interrupting the service immediately, the rabbi,

throwing a coat over his shoulders, had rushed out of the synagogue and boarded the streetcar. His assistant went with him; they were on their way to the dreaded military prison where the young Jew was being held.

Even the prison guards had heard of the great Rabbi Perlmutter. They immediately ushered him into their commander's office. The rabbi was pale and weak from fasting, but his manner was confident as he faced the commanding officer and pleaded for the young prisoner.

"Your honor, I know the young man in question personally. I can vouch for his innocence."

The rabbi's sincerity had its effect on the commanding officer. He, too, knew of the great Rabbi Perlmutter. And he knew that it was Yom Kippur, and that the rabbi had left the synagogue to plead for the prisoner.

Pointing to a piece of paper, he asked, "If I release him in your custody, will you sign this document undertaking to be responsible for him and to deliver him to us when we need him?"

The rabbi winced. How many more times would he be required to profane the solemn sanctity of this Yom Kippur? He unbuttoned his overcoat and held it wide open as he faced the officer.

"I am still wearing the *Tallit* and *Kittel* I had on when I left the House of God," he said. "Today is Yom Kippur, our holiest day. It is a day of fasting and prayer and communion with God. Writing is forbidden. I am the rabbi of the community, the leader they look up to as a model of Jewish living. But if it will save an innocent life, I'll break our holy law and sign this document."

The rabbi reached for the pen on the officer's desk. But the officer, deeply stirred by the rabbi's words and

his readiness to break the law of God for a noble purpose, moved the pen out of his reach.

"It will not be necessary," he said. "Your word is
just as good." And then the officer issued an order to the
sentry.

Soon the rabbi and his assistant, accompanied by
the freed and grateful prisoner, left the prison. But they
found that it was already completely dark. The sun had
long since set. The stars were out. It was night, and Yom
Kippur was over.

The old rabbi, weak from fasting, weary from sleep-
lessness, overwrought by his ordeal at the prison, stumbled for a moment. The assistant looked at him anxiously, and stepped into the road to engage a taxi to take the
rabbi home.

But Rabbi Perlmutter stopped him.

"What are you doing?" he said. "How can you? We
have not yet made *Havdalah*. For us it is still Yom Kippur. We can't ride. We will walk."

And slowly, through the streets of Warsaw, Rabbi
Perlmutter, who on Yom Kippur had ridden in a streetcar to save another man's life, trudged home.

Jewish Folk Tale

A Taste of the Cold

MANY years of activity in *Tzedakah* had taught Rabbi Elijah Hayim of Lodz that in order to go around collecting funds for the needy, one needed more than just a sad story to relate about a poor, unfortunate family in desperate need.

"One needed," the good rabbi would often say, "a smile to light up the sadness."

Once, during a very severe winter in Lodz, Rabbi Elijah started a campaign to buy wood and coal for the poor. The rabbi decided to start off his campaign with the wealthy Kalman Poznansky, knowing that if Poznansky gave very charitably the rest of the community would follow.

At Poznansky's house, the doorman announced the rabbi's name to his master. Instantly the wealthy Poznansky came out into the hall and greeted the rabbi cordially.

"Come. Come into the warm parlor for a glass of tea, Rabbi," he said.

But the good rabbi refused to move from the hall, even though it was very cold there and Poznansky was lightly dressed. In fact, Rabbi Elijah began a long chat on various topics—business, world conditions, synagogue affairs.

Poznansky trembled with cold; his teeth chattered. He stood it as long as he could, but finally he burst out: "Please, please, Rabbi! Come inside! I'm freezing out here in the cold hall!"

"Certainly," said the rabbi, without moving a step. "But first I want to tell you what I came for. This is a bitter cold winter, Poznansky. Snow and ice everywhere. Food and fuel so scarce and prices so high. I want a *big* contribution from you, Poznansky, to start off a collection for the poor."

"Anything! Anything!" exclaimed Poznansky—and with this promise the rabbi let himself be hustled into the warm parlor.

There Poznansky turned to him and said, "Please, Rabbi, may I ask why you kept me out there in the cold like that? Do you usually visit with people in cold halls?"

Rabbi Elijah Hayim's eyes twinkled as he unbuttoned his coat. "Well," he explained, "I've noticed that a contented man cannot really understand the sufferings of others. If we had sat down immediately in this warm, comfortable room—near that cheerful fire and with that steaming samovar waiting, full of tasty tea—would *you* have sensed even for a moment the suffering that goes on in other homes this winter?"

Poznansky began to smile.

"But when we stayed out in the cold hall," the rabbi continued, "you *did* feel just a little of what suffering is like and you were willing to give *anything* to be warm again!"

Poznansky roared with approving laughter.

The good rabbi smiled, too, and left.

Jewish Folk Tale

The Sorcery of Silver

LIKE most miserly men, Isaac was a lonely man. Rich? He was very rich; he lived only for his money. Hard-working? Very hard-working; he labored to amass wealth. Evenings he spent counting and re-counting his wealth. And all his plans were filled with schemes to acquire still more money.

Isaac showed very little interest in his own family. And so far as he was concerned, other people didn't even exist. Outside of his business matters, he kept himself apart from the entire community. Time and again his townsmen approached him, as they did everyone else, for gifts to charitable causes. To all he turned a deaf ear, so that in time he came to be called Miser Isaac.

It happened a few days before Passover that the community committee charged with gathering *Maot Hittim*, the "wheat money" intended for the baking of *Matzot* for the needy, reported to Rabbi Ezekiel that the collection was going very badly.

"Never have we had so many poor people for whom we must provide Passover needs, and never have we collected so little money for *Maot Hittim*. What shall we do, Rabbi?"

Rabbi Ezekiel was a venerable old rabbi who made it a point to acquaint himself thoroughly with all the affairs of his community. Its charitable causes were dear to his heart. And as he listened to the committee's report he felt deeply saddened.

113

"Business has been bad for more than a year," a committeeman said. "Many people have lost money, and no one can afford to give as generously as before. Everyone who could afford it gave something."

"Except Miser Isaac," said another committeeman. "Rabbi, perhaps you will talk to Isaac. We must do something for our fund."

"So many people are depending on us, Rabbi."

"Isaac is the only one in town who is making money —more and more money every day."

"If he wanted to, Rabbi, he could save the Passover holiday for the entire community and not even feel it."

"Perhaps if you spoke to him, Rabbi . . ."

Rabbi Ezekiel gazed thoughtfully at the group of men around him.

"How much money have you already gathered?" he asked.

"A thousand gulden. We need a thousand more."

The rabbi thought a moment, then spoke decisively: "I know Isaac is a very unhappy man. I will speak to him, as much for his own sake as for the fund. Summon him."

The committee members leaped to their feet. They hurried off to tell Isaac that the rabbi wanted to see him.

Isaac received the message with mingled feelings. It was an honor, of course, to be summoned by the great Rabbi Ezekiel, but on the other hand how could he leave his business affairs in the middle of the day? Every minute away from his business would mean money lost. Moreover, just what did the rabbi want to see him about?

The rabbi's invitation was a command and it could not be ignored. And so, regretfully, he instructed his assistants on various matters and set out for the rabbi's home.

On his arrival the rabbi greeted him warmly: "Come in, come in, Isaac. Make yourself at home. Here—sit down in this chair."

"Rabbi, it is a great honor," began Isaac. "I don't deserve . . ."

"Deserve?" interrupted the rabbi. "Of course you deserve. It is a rabbi's duty to interest himself in the welfare of his people, and I am afraid I have neglected you. Tell me, Isaac, are you happy?"

The abrupt question took Isaac by surprise. "Happy? Well—ah—happy, eh? Who is happy, Rabbi? Who —can know what happiness . . ."

Again the rabbi interrupted him, repeating the question quietly: "Are you happy, Isaac?"

Isaac looked into the rabbi's deep eyes for a moment, then shifted his gaze uncomfortably to the ground. He was silent for a long time, and then he spoke in an almost inaudible voice: "Rabbi Ezekiel, I am not happy at all. I am wretched."

The rabbi nodded kindly. "I know, Isaac. That is why I asked you. But why aren't you happy? You are the envy of all. You are by far the richest man in town. Your wealth grows daily. You have enough money to gratify the wildest desire. Your family is secure forever from want and poverty. How can you be unhappy?"

"Oh, Rabbi, I have thought about it often, and I do not know. Yes, I am rich. Yes, I have everything and can get anything money can buy. When I was a poor

boy I was sure happiness lay in wealth. I still think this
is so—but despite my riches I am the most miserable
man in the community. Why, Rabbi? Why? Can you
tell me? Please tell me if you can."

Rabbi Ezekiel said nothing for a long moment, then
he arose and went over to the window. "Come here,
Isaac," he said.

Obediently, Isaac took his place at the rabbi's
side.

"Look out the window, Isaac. What do you see?"

Isaac glanced out the window and said, "I see the
market place."

"But what do you see *in* the market place?" insisted Rabbi Ezekiel.

Isaac examined the sight outside the window long and carefully. Then he said: "I see people—old and young, men and women. All of them are poorly dressed. All of them are clearly poor. I cannot see a single person who looks as if he had any money at all."

"Yes," said the rabbi. "Many poor people is what you see through the window-pane. Now look at this mirror

on the wall. What do you see now?"

"Why—myself, of course."

"Of course. You look through the window and see many poor people. You look into the mirror and you see only yourself. Why, Isaac? Window and mirror are both made of the same kind of glass."

"But the mirror is a mirror," said Isaac.

"Yes, but the question is—what makes it a mirror?"

Isaac looked at the rabbi with puzzled eyes, wondering what he was leading up to.

"A curtain of silver," explained the rabbi, "was added to a plain sheet of glass, and it became a mirror. Just a little silver was added, that is all, and yet it changes the entire view. That, Isaac, is the sorcery of silver. And that, too, is the sorcery of money. Without money we see people. With a thin silver curtain before our eyes, with a little money in our purse, we are bewitched by its sorcery, and we see only ourselves. Once you saw people. Today, with your wealth, you can see only yourself. You are bewitched, Isaac. Who can be happy when he is bewitched?"

Isaac seemed stunned. Again he looked out of the window, again into the mirror. Then he looked at the rabbi, and found that he was unable to meet his eye. Suddenly he sank into a chair and began to weep.

When Isaac left Rabbi Ezekiel an hour later, he already seemed a much happier man. The rabbi, too, was happy. For one thing, he had two thousand more gulden for the *Maot Hittim* fund. For another thing, and a far more important one, he had saved a soul in Israel.

Jewish Folk Tale

WE CARRY ON

In the New Land

Early every morning, Rabbi Henry Cohen, of Galveston, Texas, marked a list of names on his shirt cuffs—his daily appointments with people who needed help. It didn't matter whether the person was white or negro, Jew or Christian. He raced around on his bicycle with his coat tails flying, performing errands of good deeds.

One day, a Russian named Lemchuk, who was detained by the immigration authorities, sent for Rabbi Cohen. He had escaped from Russia and had entered the United States illegally. The law required that the immigration officials send him back. His only crime in Russia had been speaking out against the government, for which he would be exiled for life to Siberia or shot before a firing squad. The immigration authorities had no choice but to carry out the law. They were planning to send him back on the next boat. In desperation the man appealed to Rabbi Cohen.

"You help everybody else, Rabbi," he pleaded, "please help me too. Only you can save me from death or life-long imprisonment in Siberia."

Rabbi Cohen rushed away to a friend, borrowed a hundred dollars for train fare, and caught the next train to Washington, D. C.

On the train memories of his last visit to Washington passed through his mind. He had been invited to submit a fitting inscription for the figure of "Judea," which typified "Religion"—Judaism's contribution to civilization. This figure had been prepared for the rotunda of the cen-

tral reading room of the Library of Congress. It repre-
sented a woman, her hands lifted up in prayer, a scroll
on her lap, and on her right a tablet of stone on which
the inscription was to be made. At first he suggested
Hillel's Golden Rule, "Do not do to your neighbor what
you would not have done unto you." But the artist ex-
pressed a preference for the phrase in the Book of Le-
viticus, chapter 19, verse 18, "Love your neighbor as
yourself." He agreed that the Biblical verse, inscribed in
Hebrew, was more suited to adorn the figure in the Con-
gressional Library.

A glow of pride suffused him. To think that he,
Henry Cohen, a recent immigrant, was singled out for
this honor by his adopted land. This is what America will
always mean: life, liberty and the pursuit of happiness.
It must not let Lemchuk down!

As soon as he arrived in Washington, he rushed to
the Immigration Office.

"I am sorry I can't do anything," the chief said, "the
law is clear. The deportation papers have already been
signed."

Rabbi Cohen, realizing that his efforts were of no
avail, presented himself to his Congressman who arranged for an appointment at the White House.

President Taft received him cordially but his answer
was still no. Even the President's hands were tied, particularly when the Immigration Department had already
acted to deport the man. But the President was im-
pressed by the grief and misery that clouded Rabbi
Cohen's face. "You Jews are certainly a great people," he
said. "It's wonderful how far you will go to help one another—to help a member of your faith in trouble."

"Mr. President," Rabbi Cohen broke in sharply. "This poor fellow isn't a Jew, he's a Greek Catholic."

The President jumped to his feet in astonishment. "A *Catholic?*" he repeated. "You mean to tell me you came up all the way from Galveston to Washington at your own expense to appeal for a *Christian?*"

"Certainly," said Rabbi Cohen. "He is in trouble; he asked me to help him. He'll face a firing squad when he gets back to Russia. He is a human being; a human life is at stake, Mr. President. What difference does his religion make?"

The President stared at him for a moment, then abruptly lifted his telephone and called his secretary. "Take a telegram," he said, "to the Chief Inspector of Immigration in Galveston: 'Hold Lemchuk in Galveston and release him in the custody of Rabbi Cohen on his return. You will hear directly from the Immigration Department.' Then sign my name."

Then he came over to Rabbi Cohen, placed his hands on his shoulders, and gently urged him to sit down again.

"Now, tell me all about yourself," said the President. "I want to hear all about what goes on in Galveston."

"But, Mr. President," protested the Rabbi, "you're a busy man . . . your appointments . . ."

The President waved his hand. "If you could do what you've done, I can spare a little time to learn how I can help you in your work in Texas."

Adapted from "The Man Who Stayed In Texas,"
by Anne Nathan and Harry I. Cohen

Keeping Our Promise

A<small>T FIRST</small>, *Tzedakah* in America centered around the synagogue, as it had in the Old World. For example, the Spanish and Portuguese Synagogue of New York City authorized its president to give out small amounts freely from synagogue funds, for any worthy cause; and where large amounts were involved, he discussed the matter with the trustees and acted on their advice. The Synagogue also had its own pension system, and cared for the ill, the aged, the disabled, and the unemployed. It distributed to the entire community *Matzot* for Passover, fuel in winter, and provided medical aid and free burial.

In 1850 the non-Jews themselves used to say that nobody ever saw a Jewish beggar on the streets of New York. And in other cities, the same proud tradition of *Tzedakah* was carried on by the Jewish community.

Tzedakah Branches Out

In the year 1820, when a Jewish veteran of the Revolutionary War lay seriously ill in a hospital in New York City, a group of Jews raised a fund to help him. The giving had been so generous that when the hero died a sum of three hundred dollars still remained in the fund. The decision of these men about what to do with the money was to become historic. They organized the Hebrew Benevolent Society, whose purpose was to continue helping needy people, and whose Hebrew name—The Restorer of the Soul—reminds us of the picturesque names of such societies in the Middle Ages.

Later on, a great American Jew, Mordecai Manuel Noah, became its president. Under his leadership the society grew until the original three hundred dollars had increased to many thousands.

In time, other Jews organized similar societies—the German Hebrew Benevolent Society was one example —all of them separate from the synagogues (which still continued to carry on their own programs of relief). As more and more Jews arrived in America, the number of the societies increased. Some—such as the Bachelors' Loan Society, the Young Men's Fuel Association, and the Society for Educating Orphan Children—were organized to help one particular group of needy people. Women's organizations—among them the Female Hebrew Benevolent Society, the Order of True Sisters, and the many sewing societies that provided clothing to the poor —became especially important. Sometimes, too, people from the same town or country in Europe would organize a general welfare society to make loans, find jobs, provide education and social activities, and take care of all relief needs of their own group.

The Federation Idea

America was the land of freedom and opportunity, and Jews by the hundreds of thousands migrated here. Most of them, of course, came first to New York, the country's greatest port. Many were penniless, and all needed to find jobs. Disease, epidemics and financial depressions were harder on these people than on most others. The immigrants had to learn a new language and new ways of living, and often a new trade. They also had to be encouraged to go inland to other cities.

The many local societies and synagogues began to find that they could not handle the tremendous job of helping these people by their separate efforts. And thus, sixty years ago, the Jewish Federation idea was born, setting an example that was followed by non-sectarian Community Chests twenty years ago. Its aim was to join many welfare societies into one big federation. There would be one campaign for funds, and one board of directors to decide how and where the money was to be spent on the basis of careful study of the needs and services, related to the urgency of problems and the importance of purposes.

The Federation idea has prevented waste and duplication. It has made possible community planning and coordinating. It has enabled the Jewish community to do a better job of *Tzedakah*. For example, as a city changes and as people move out of some neighborhoods and into others, only a single, united federation can plan for new institutions and new buildings. When there is a crisis or emergency in Jewish life, only a single, united federation can bring the entire Jewish community together quickly as a co-ordinated team.

Beginning with World War I the Jews of America were called upon to do more than take care of their own. The American Jewish community, which had risen from very humble beginnings, became the most important community in the world. It came to the rescue of its brothers overseas. It accepted leadership and responsibility in providing relief and help for the war sufferers and refugees overseas and for the upbuilding of Palestine (now Israel).

Today our Jewish communities everywhere carry on

a double task: caring for those at home and for our people abroad.

At home the Federation network includes a broad range of agencies and services, supported by the entire community and operating in behalf of the entire community. They include hospitals and clinics, family welfare and child care, Jewish schools and cultural organizations, homes for the aged, vocational guidance, Jewish community centers, summer camps, workshops for the handicapped, agencies concerned with civil rights, etc. The Federation, or Welfare Fund, also supports agencies working in Israel, in Europe and in other lands.

Thus in America, in Israel, in Europe, the many modern heroes of *Tzedakah*—worthy heirs of the Golden Thread—still act by the most ancient ideals of their faith.